Revolution in Light

LASERS AND HOLOGRAPHY

Revolution in Light

LASERS AND HOLOGRAPHY

by

IRWIN STAMBLER

Garden City, New York
DOUBLEDAY & COMPANY, INC.

PHOTO CREDITS

Hughes Aircraft Company; 1, 6, 7, 8, 10, 19, 21, 22, 26, 27, 32, 33, 34, 35, 38, 47, 48, 54
General Electric; 2, 3, 4, 23
RCA; 5, 50, 51, 52, 53, 55
Bell Laboratories; 9, 13, 24, 25, 29, 39, 49
Conductron Corporation; 11, 12
TRW Systems; 14, 15, 20, 36
McDonnell Douglas; 16, 17
Holosonics, Inc.; 18, 60
Aerojet-General; 18A
Perkin-Elmer Corporation; 28
Aerospace Corporation; 30, 31
Apollo Lasers; 37
IBM; 40, 41
Lockheed Missiles & Space Company; 42
National Engineering Science Company; 43
Electro-Optical Systems; 44, 45, 46
Honeywell; 56, 57, 58
Battelle-Northwest; 59

ISBN: 0-385-00506-7 TRADE
0-385-01886-X PREBOUND
Library of Congress Catalog Card Number 75–157428
9 8 7 6 5 4 3 2

Contents

ACKNOWLEDGMENTS

I would like to express my appreciation for the help un-stintingly given me by many people in industry and research organizations in preparing this book. Among those people and organizations who have been most helpful are Doug Diltz, George Caulfield, Bill Herrmann, Hughes Aircraft Corporation and Research Laboratories, Honeywell Corporation, Conductron Corporation, Harry Calkins, McDonnell Douglas Corporation, Lockheed Aircraft Corporation, TRW Systems, the editors of *Industrial Research* magazine, Aerospace Corporation, General Electric, IBM, Bell Telephone Laboratories, Don Raymond, General Telephone and Electronics, RCA Corporation, Tom Tugend, University of California at Los Angeles, National Aeronautics and Space Administration, Autonetics Division of North American Rockwell, William Bushor and the editorial staff of *Lasersphere* magazine, and Dr. Theodore Maiman.

I would particularly like to thank Dr. Maiman and William Bushor for reviewing the manuscript for technical accuracy.

IRWIN STAMBLER

Beverly Hills, California
1971

CHAPTER I

MAKING COHERENT LIGHT

For a moment, settle back and imagine you are in the family room of the future. It doesn't look too different from the home entertainment center of today—there are bookshelves, a radio, and what seems to be a TV set. You pick up a remote control handset, turn it to a channel number—and suddenly the room is transformed in a completely unexpected way. From the TV set a picture appears, then expands to seemingly fill the room. You are not just looking at the scene, you are in it.

The moving images are all around you. A cavalry charge thunders past, and you can almost feel the choking dust rising in clouds from the countless hoofbeats. Or you dial a travel scene and walk along the streets of some distant city or are transported to a far-off point of interest. Next you might choose the home drama channel where the action leaves place for you to take a part, declaiming the speech of an important character or joining dancers in some intricate choreography. Of course you know it isn't real; you can pass your hand right through the people or buildings. But it is completely lifelike, with the features of the objects in the scene changing as you walk around them just as they would if you moved from one place to the other in the actual location.

To the reader of science fiction, the situation just described does not seem startling. But it is true that even in this complex age, it is hard to imagine it as anything but fiction. However, the basic theories that could lead to these three-dimensional TV movies are proven fact today. As we shall see in later pages, they already have been demonstrated on a small scale. It is just one of many spectacular new advancements promised by a series of discoveries we might call the Revolution in Light.

This is a revolution that is still in its infancy. The actual operation of the main factor in this new technology, the laser, only occurred in 1960. On May 15 of that year, a young physicist named Theodore H. Maiman crouched before a small device on a laboratory table at Hughes Aircraft Company in Culver City, California. He turned on a switch, activating a powerful flash lamp wound in a coil around a tiny red-colored rod. To the naked eye, besides the sudden pulse of light in the flash lamp, nothing happened. But as Maiman studied a series of measuring instruments, examining the wavy lines made on a chart by a device called a spectrograph, he knew he had achieved a tiny, hard to see beam of light that was unlike any that man had derived before. This was a beam of intensity far greater than any light ray that ever existed on earth, the first "coherent" light.

The laser principle is based on the use of an outside energy source to stimulate changes in energy patterns in the atoms or molecules of specially selected materials. This technique is summed up as Light Amplification by Stimulated Emission of Radiation. The initial letters of

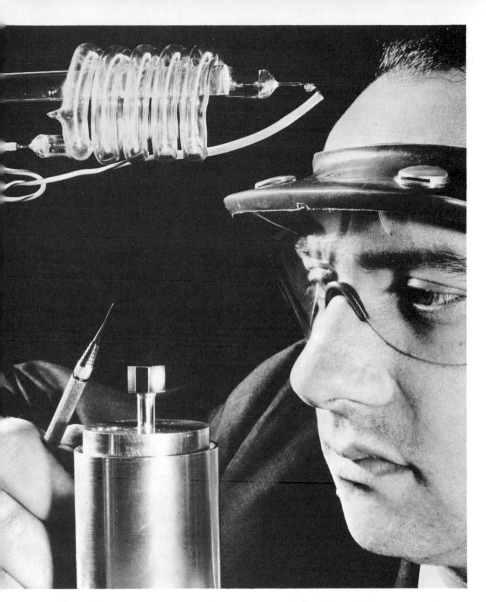

1. *Dr. Theodore Maiman, the scientist who built and demonstrated the first operating laser, examines key parts of his device. At the bottom, he studies a cube of synthetic ruby crystal. The coiled tube at top is the light-producing part of the powerful quartz lamp used to excite chromium ions of the ruby to the energy levels needed for coherent light.*

this phrase provide the acronym "laser." The laser has also been called an "optical maser" (the maser will be discussed later in this chapter), but this designation is not too much used today. Some scientists also coined the acronym "loser," for Light Oscillator by Stimulated Emission of Radiation, but this has been discarded as not being a proper description of a device that has been so eminently successful.

The first laser beam was invisible to the eye because the first transparent rod of synthetic ruby had been crudely made by a machine shop outfitted for aerospace work rather than precision optics. Within a few weeks' time, Maiman and his co-workers had obtained a precision-formed ruby rod fabricated by optical technology, and this time the laser beam not only could be detected by instruments, but could be easily observed as a very thin, intensely bright ray of light coming from one end of the device.

To someone glancing at the laser for the first time, this thin beam might not have been very impressive, but to scientists who knew the nature of the phenomenon, it was a breakthrough as great as any in the long history of science and technology. The laser beam captured within its small envelope tremendous amounts of energy, energy that could be used for many different things, from drilling minute holes in the hardest material known to man—the diamond—to carrying billions of different voice signals on a single laser beam.

Progress in laser technology was so rapid that within three to four years after Maiman's achievement, a few practical applications were already at hand. On assembly lines in aircraft factories, for instance, laser beams were used to line up plane production tools to accuracies of thousandths of an inch. And, by then, scientists in laboratories throughout the world were studying hundreds of different kinds of lasers for a wide range of possible uses in the future.

As Maiman says, it was hard for many people to believe that a working laser could be made. Right up to the time he demonstrated his device, some experts said it couldn't be done. "The principles of the laser were not new, of course, they had been proposed by a number of scientists in previous years. The question was whether anyone could build a device that could take the jumbled light waves normally turned out by a light source and line them up in a single concentrated beam of only one frequency. The very time that I was preparing to try my first laser test, one scientist in the Midwest was completing a technical paper proving a working laser violated scientific principles."

The basic principles of the laser, though, had already been demonstrated for other parts of the electromagnetic spectrum. Simply speaking, these principles indicated that by designing the proper kind of equipment it was possible to take an electromagnetic wave and amplify it—that is, increase its strength so the wave coming out of the device was more intense than the original wave. It was this amplifying effect, for instance, demonstrated by Dr. Lee de Forest on radio waves in 1907, that made modern radio and TV practical. (De Forest used a series of electrodes in a vacuum tube to change a weak radio signal to a strong one.)

Radio waves form one part of an entire "universe" of energy waves called the electromagnetic spectrum. Without

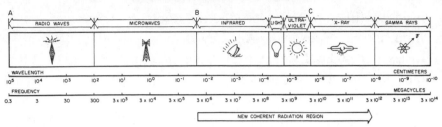

2. Chart of the electromagnetic spectrum indicates the region in which masers and lasers operate. As the chart shows, much of the operating range of these devices is outside the visible light region.

understanding exactly why this is so, scientists have found that the cosmos is constantly pulsing with an infinite number of vibrations or waves. Originally, almost all of these energy waves occurred naturally, like the waves of the ocean or the various waves of radiation flowing from the sun. In the fairly recent past, man learned how to produce some of these waves himself from special techniques and equipment.

Depending on the source, electromagnetic waves can have different properties of wave form, but all of them travel in space at the same speed, the speed of light (approximately 186,000 miles/sec.*). The waves can be classified either by their wavelength or frequency. The frequency refers to the number of times a particular energy wave repeats itself in a specific amount of time: usually frequency is quoted in number of cycles per second. The length of the wave means exactly that, the over-all

* The exact speed of light in a vacuum, such as space, is 186,282.0. However, the speed in air varies slightly with color and the speed of light in other media, such as glass, is considerably different from that in vacuum.

distance (usually given in centimeters) from the beginning of one wave cycle to the end of that cycle.

A chart of the electromagnetic spectrum shows that radio waves are at the low frequency end, and that wave frequency increases if one moves through the spectrum to the high-frequency gamma rays produced by nuclear reactions. Though not shown on the chart, the radio wave spectrum is further subdivided into short wave, very high frequency, and ultra high frequency. It will be recognized that the last two, VHF and UHF, are the frequencies in which television systems operate. After a broad band of frequencies called microwaves come a series of frequencies called infrared, visible, and ultraviolet. The laser can be made to work in all of the last three energy ranges.

It was relatively easy to work with radio waves because, as generated by electron tubes, these generally have a single, definite frequency. Above this band, things get more complex. Light waves, for instance, occur in nature as a mixture of waves. The reason is that light waves are generated by many individual atoms or molecules, each of which emits radiation for a short interval and then is followed by others at a slightly different frequency. So before the advent of the laser, all sources of light were incoherent and therefore very difficult to use efficiently.

Though scientists did not realize it at first, the way to gain this efficiency was indicated by a body of theory expounded by Dr. Albert Einstein in 1917. Implicit in his theory is the fact that an electromagnetic wave interacting with an atom could stimulate the atom to emit a basic unit of light, called a photon, having the same wavelength as the electromagnetic wave. When this happens, the result is the addition of energy to the original electromagnetic wave, thus producing amplification. The name given to this process is stimulated emission.

However, Einstein did not suggest a way in which this emission could be done in an actual device, nor did anyone else figure out a method for over forty years. The principle of stimulated emission was used, though, to amplify waves of a lower frequency region, that of microwaves. Even this did not occur until after World War II.

Why did it take so long? Mainly the delay was caused by a lack of research on the microwave spectrum. During World War II, the invention of radar opened up a new chapter in electromagnetics. By the end of World War II, scientists around the world were studying underlying microwave theory, and some of them realized it might be possible to use the principle of stimulated emission to amplify microwave energy. Among those who suggested this possibility in the early 1950s were Russian scientists Nikolai G. Basov and Alexander M. Prokhorov and American researchers Dr. Charles H. Townes of Columbia University and Dr. Joseph Weber of the University of Maryland.

In 1954, Professor Townes and and his associates, Drs. James P. Gordon and Herbert J. Zeiger, won the race to demonstrate the first maser. (The acronym maser represents the first letters of the words in Microwave Amplification by Stimulated Emission of Radiation.) They based their system on a molecule of ammonia and the fact that an ammonia atom can be raised, or "pumped," from a low energy level to a higher energy level. The atom at the higher energy level is unstable—like water pumped to a storage tank, it tends to fall back down to its lower "rest" state. When the atom or molecule "falls" to the lower state, it emits a particle of energy called a photon, whose energy is exactly equal to the difference in energy between the two states.

If this photon collides with an atom in the lower state and the photon matches the difference in energy levels, the photon will be absorbed and the atom will be excited to the higher energy state. In this case, though, no amplification occurs. On the other hand, if this photon collides with an atom in the higher state and the energy matches, an extra photon is emitted. In this case, the result is two photons instead of one. As this suggests, for

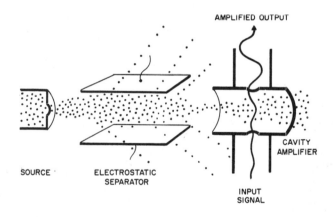

3. *Diagram of the main parts of the first maser (Microwave Amplification by Stimulated Emission of Radiation) invented by Charles H. Townes, Herbert J. Zeiger, and James P. Gordon at Columbia University. Excited molecules of ammonia are separated out in the separator and passed into a special metal box called a microwave cavity. When an electronic signal in the microwave range is directed into the cavity, energy from the excited gas particles is given up to the incoming beam, increasing the beam's strength so that the signal going out is much stronger than the original signal.*

amplification to occur, the atoms or molecules of the material must be arranged so that there are more particles of matter in the higher energy state than the lower. When this kind of "population inversion" is achieved, a beam of photons passed through the material will produce extra photons, causing the output wave to have more photons than the input beam.

In Townes' ammonia maser, a stream of ammonia gas was passed through a non-uniform electric field that separated high energy molecules from low energy ones. The high energy molecules then were beamed into a metal box with highly reflecting walls called a "microwave cavity." Then microwaves of the proper frequency were fed into the cavity to interact with the gas molecules and produce photons. The photon collision effect was greatly increased by the highly reflective cavity walls. Like Ping-pong balls, photons bounced back from these walls to collide with more molecules and produce still more photons. The waves produced by this action were coherent—that is, in phase with the original driving microwave signal. The result was an amplified electromagnetic signal at the output end of the device.

Later, it was shown that other materials could be used to provide maser action, including other gases and solid materials. From a scientific standpoint, the maser was a major breakthrough. However, it has had relatively little practical application. Because the maser does not have streams of electrons, it generates very little noise. This means, for instance, that it can detect very weak signals such as those coming from stars and galaxies billions of miles away. For this reason, the maser is of great importance to radio astronomers who add to man's knowledge by studying these natural radio waves. To gain this low noise property, though, the maser must be cooled to the temperature of liquid helium—452° F. And, not long after the invention of the maser, electronic devices, called parametric amplifiers, were invented that are almost as quiet as masers, but which can work at room temperature.

It was the realization of the limited uses of the masers that caused Dr. Theodore Maiman to change course from maser development work to higher frequency experiments. Though Maiman gained his doctorate in physics from Stanford University, he had taken his master's degree in electrical engineering. As he notes, "I always had this strong interest in engineering from the age of twelve, when I ran a little electrical appliance repair store in Denver, Colorado. Actually, I had worked in my spare time for the owner, soldering wires and doing the other things needed to repair toasters, radios, and motors. When the owner went into the service, I was competent enough to run his shop for him." In his teens, Maiman worked at several other engineering jobs during vacation periods before starting college. When he reached graduate school, his electrical engineering experience made him a valuable assistant to his professors, for he could turn some of the abstract theories developed by physicists into working equipment. At the time the first maser was announced Maiman had completed several important experiments for Nobel Laureate Dr. Willis Lamb in optical and microwave technology as part of the work for his Ph.D. thesis.

As Maiman stresses, "The combination of physics and engineering I felt to be an invaluable combination.

Though my work might deal with complex theory, such as that involved in quantum electronics,* I always had the practical bent of my electrical design experience. I was still an engineer working to make something more compact and more efficient."

By the mid 1950s Maiman was applying this background to maser work at Hughes Aircraft. In particular, he redesigned a maser that used a solid ruby crystal for amplication to greatly improve its properties. "I was given the job of developing this maser for military communications work along conventional lines. I reasoned it could be done in much more practical fashion. No one asked for this; in fact, no one believed it could be done. But I used the engineering approach to do such things as replacing a huge external magnet with a small internally located permanent magnet. The final design proved to be roughly a fifth the size of the original proposal and a factor of ten better in performance.

"As I progressed, though, I began to have doubts about doing more maser work. The cooling problem and the appearance of strong competing devices made me feel it wasn't a practical system. So I became interested in the

---

* Both the maser and laser are products of the theories of the field known as quantum electronics. Quantum physics is based on a relatively new understanding of the way energy can be released. In conventional electronics, systems make use of the fact that electrons can be broken free from their orbits around the nucleus of an atom and caused to flow from one atom to another. However, scientists came to realize that electrons do not need to break their atomic bonds to absorb or release energy. This can be done by changing the relative relationships of electrons within the bounds of their atomic or molecular systems. For instance, in the laser, the change in energy levels discussed in this chapter is accomplished by moving an electron from one orbit around the nucleus to a higher one. When the electron moves from this temporary orbit back to its original one, it releases a certain amount of energy.

possibility of extending the basic technique of stimulated emission to much higher frequencies. I thought it might be feasible to extend it at least to the infrared spectrum and perhaps higher. About this time—mid 1958—Schawlow and Townes presented their paper dealing with concepts for high frequency systems."

The paper presented by Dr. Townes and his brother-in-law, Dr. Arthur Schawlow, a scientist at Bell Laboratories, was the first one published to propose the possibility of stimulated emission in the optical range. Many writers have used this paper as the basis for crediting them with invention of the laser. But Dr. Maiman has pointed to inconsistencies in such a conclusion. For one thing, at the time, Schawlow and Townes simply suggested a high frequency device was possible; they did not have a working system.

As Maiman points out, "Separately and a little after this, Schawlow gave a paper in which he discussed the possible use of a ruby crystal in a laser. He analyzed the energy requirements to provide the desired level of optical pumping to raise the crystal atoms to the high energy level. In effect, he rejected the ruby, stating no devices were available that could provide this pumping action."

Says Maiman, "Their concept was a special one. They proposed to pump a potassium vapor with a potassium lamp and obtain a match between the radiation from the potassium emitted from the vapor cell. I examined their paper and decided for several reasons not to go that route:

"First, since Schawlow and Townes and a number of scientists at other facilities were trying to make this approach work, I didn't want to just repeat other people's work.

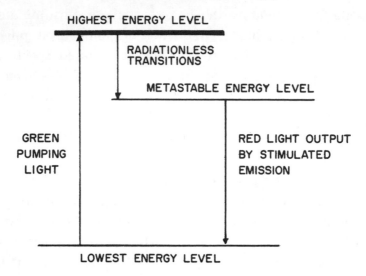

4. *Laser action is based on the fact that atoms of certain elements can be raised to a variety of energy levels. This diagram represents what happens in a simple ruby laser system. In this case, the ruby is made of crystalline aluminum oxide in which a small percentage of the aluminum atoms are replaced by particles of chromium. It is the chromium ions that produce the laser effect. These ions are excited to a higher energy level when exposed to the proper wavelength of light. The initial energy level, though, is unstable, and the ions fall back to an intermediate level which is more stable than the higher level but less stable than the original starting level. When ions from this metastable level are induced to return to the low level, they emit energy spontaneously—in this case in the form of red light.*

"More important, my engineering background made me decide, from the descriptions in their paper, that it wasn't really practical. Their own calculations indicated the potassium system was marginal or submarginal. That is, calculations showed this material system either had just enough higher energy level to permit stimulated emission or it might miss this requirement by a small percentage. In addition, I could also see it would pose tremendous problems trying to work with potassium vapor under the vacuum conditions needed inside the chamber.

"Thinking it through, I felt it would be better to try to work with solids. This seemed a cleaner way to go, and it was a different approach than that taken by other scientists. There was another consideration. A solid system was a more practical one from an engineering standpoint because it could be built more ruggedly. The question, of course, was whether I could find any kind of solid system that would work with optical pumping technology.

"I got the idea of performing some experiments with ruby. I was familiar with its properties and had pieces of ruby around. I wasn't sure that ruby was the material that would do the job. In fact, I had been persuaded by evidence presented by others that the ruby was an unlikely candidate for the operating laser. But ruby did have interesting properties, including its use in masers, that might provide a clue to which way to go. I decided to use it as a model to see what would happen."

As Maiman points out, he might have demonstrated the first laser considerably before 1960, were it not for the overwhelming weight of expert opinion that the ruby laser was all but impossible. Ironically, one of the most telling arguments against the ruby evolved from Maiman's old research group at Stanford; in fact, the paper outlining these data was presented by a physicist then working at Westinghouse, trained by Maiman to take over his Stanford experiments.

"The Westinghouse paper indicated the quantum effi-

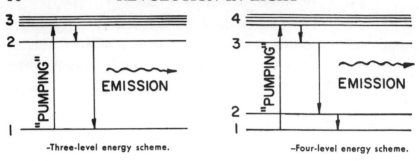

-Three-level energy scheme.   –Four-level energy scheme.

5. Laser systems can be more complex than the diagram shown for a simple ruby. Some types of ions can be excited to levels from which there are two, three, or more intermediate levels of stability as indicated in these diagrams.

ciency of ruby was very low—in the neighborhood of 1 per cent. This was so low you certainly could never develop an optical pumping system to get the required number of atoms to a higher energy level needed for lasing. I had no reason to doubt the low ruby efficiency. I had trained the man who presented the paper and knew he was an excellent experimenter. In addition, at the first Quantum Physics Symposium held that year, Schawlow gave data which also made the use of the ruby for lasing seem a very remote eventuality."

At this point, the history of the laser hung in the balance. It was difficult for Maiman to ignore the weight of opinion. He could have rejected any work with ruby and delayed the start of laser technology by years or even decades. For days and weeks he turned the matter over in his mind, wondering which direction to go or whether it was worth experimenting at all.

"My feelings were—yes, this looks hard to do, but before rejecting the ruby outright, practical engineering made me decide to calculate the energy requirements involved to see if it was really impossible. What I came up with indicated it was difficult, but could be done, except for the efficiency problem.

"This indicated it would require raising 100 atoms to an excited level to get one to come back down as fluorescent light. This certainly would be intolerable. So I thought I'd better look for another material than ruby, but to do this, it seemed to make sense to find out where the 99 per cent loss of efficiency occurred in the ruby system. I could then use this information to find a material without this problem."

Maiman carefully studied what was required for his experiment, set up the measuring instruments and the crystal sample to precise standards. "When I began a long series of tests to find the places where the ruby problems occurred, I couldn't find anything. It slowly began to dawn on me that there might have been some errors in the earlier data. It was an extremely tricky experiment to conduct and minor errors in the many variables involved could

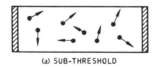 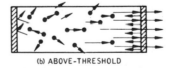

(a) SUB-THRESHOLD   (b) ABOVE-THRESHOLD

6. The important thing that occurs in a laser is the achievement of coherent light. Before atoms in a lasing material reach the coherent energy level, the light rays go off in all directions as at the left. Once the excited atoms are raised above the lasing threshold, all the atoms leaving the laser line up in the same direction (right) creating a compact, intense light beam.

cause major discrepancies in the results. Finally, I repeated the original test and found the efficiency to be at least 70 per cent. I went back over the earlier data and found, to my satisfaction, where the key mistake had been made. Now I was sure—the ruby was a promising laser material!"

Despite all the data, though, Maiman was uncertain about proceeding. Knowing that ruby potentially had the needed properties was one thing, devising a system to turn these into an actual laser was something else. In particular, the system required a very strong light source to provide the pumping action to get the crystal atoms to a higher energy level.

Recalls Maiman, "The pressures were intense. The people I worked with told me it wouldn't work. I kept imagining the reactions I would incur if I went ahead and built the equipment and failed. I could have done it in a month or two after my experiments that revised the ruby information, but I did not want to look foolish. I proceeded with very great caution."

Maiman's first step was to try to find a special lamp to do the pumping. He calculated and recalculated the kinetic energy equations that provided insight into what kind of light output was needed. "I discovered that the most important parameter of the pumping lamp wasn't its total power output, or the length of the ruby, or any of several other factors. Instead, the really important property was its brightness."

With this information in hand, Maiman began to search through every catalogue for high intensity lamps he could obtain. Some literature was already in his files or in the company library; others were urgently requested by mail or phone from major lamp manufacturers. After poring over this literature for many hours and running calculations of dozens of different light sources, Maiman concluded the only readily available lamp with the right brightness was a special kind of mercury vapor lamp.

"But even with the best mercury vapor device and using the most efficient pumping geometries, I decided the experiment probably would work, but it seemed almost as marginal as the potassium system of Schawlow and Townes. So I decided I wouldn't do it.

"With hindsight, it's now obvious that if I had proceeded at the time, I could have made a system that would work. But I was timorous. As far as anyone knew, no one had made a laser, no one knew how to make a laser, and the question was just as pertinent: would anyone ever be able to make one? But with a system that seemed marginal on paper, it seemed to be taking too much of a chance to commit a great deal of time and laboratory apparatus. I asked myself—suppose I set everything up and it didn't work? This could lead to termination of the program, and I would never know if I had gotten to within a fraction of a per cent of actually achieving laser action.

"Anyway, I wasn't willing to stick my neck out and fail in this way. I went back to my books, catalogues, and calculations to see if there was another way to do it. This led to the idea of using a xenon flash lamp. This lamp, it turns out, is not as good as the mercury vapor one in some properties, but its brightness is much greater." The xenon lamp had the drawback that it did not operate continuously. The lamp was designed for aerial reconnaissance work; to gain its intensely bright light without burning up, it could only be pulsed to run for short periods of time.

However, it promised a margin of 6 or 7 per cent for the lasing process instead of only 1–1½ or less for the mercury vapor device.

Even then Maiman's choice was limited. After examining every lamp listed in every catalogue, he found only three that had the desired brightness, all made by General Electric. When he explained his needs to General Electric lighting engineers, they made some suggestions that simplified his experiments. They suggested that since brightness was the main concern, Maiman might as well just place his equipment near the lamp rather than building special reflectors to focus the light to a point source.

Considering this, and noting that the flash lamp comes in the form of a spring-shaped glass spiral, Maiman decided he could make his equipment even more compact by placing the ruby crystal inside the spiral.

The result was a device that was no larger than a small transistor radio. The first laser was so small and prosaic-looking, in fact, that editors and reporters who attended the first press conference announcing the new wonder thought the whole thing might be a hoax.

Still worrying about sufficient margin, Maiman thought of a way to increase the brightness directed at the ruby still more. "I remembered that if you heat a filament to a certain temperature, you eventually reach a balance between temperature and the rate of energy radiated into the surrounding environment. So I decided if I placed a highly silvered radiation shield around the lamp there would be no increase in power, but the source would become much brighter because the shield would prevent it from radiating as well."

Finally, the time had come to begin assembling the apparatus. He selected a ruby from those on hand and gave the laboratory machinists instructions as to how to shape it. He also decided on the use of a silver coating on either end of the rod for reflecting plates. These plates are used to reflect beams of spontaneous emission light back and

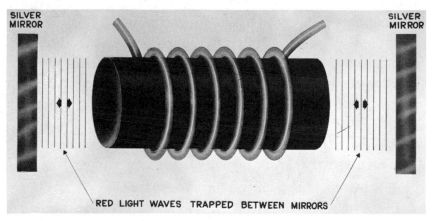

7. *Exploded view of the ruby laser system invented by Dr. Theodore Maiman of Hughes Aircraft Company. The silver mirrors actually are located on the ends of the ruby rod rather than some distance away.*

forth within the rod. With each pass, the stream of photons causes an increasing number of atoms in the higher energy level to cascade down to the lower level. With each trip from one reflecting plate to the other, the strength of the radiation grows, leading up to the production of the intense beam on monochromatic light that is the laser's output.

The coatings on the two ends are not exactly the same. One coating is so thick it will not allow any light to pass through it. The other coating must be semi-transparent so that it will allow a beam to go through it when the light intensity reaches the desired level. Maiman recalls, "I wanted to put a heavy silver coating on one end and a semi-transparent one on the other, but the shop had a hard job applying the thinner coating. So finally I put heavy coatings on both ends but left a thin hole in the coating on one end to couple out the energy."

By mid May of 1960, all the parts were ready and Maiman carefully put them together in a section of the Hughes facility in Culver City, California. He attached special detectors, including a device called a spectrograph. On May 15, all was ready to go. Still, Maiman admits he felt hesitant about starting the experiment. "I had been afraid that all my theorizing and studying might

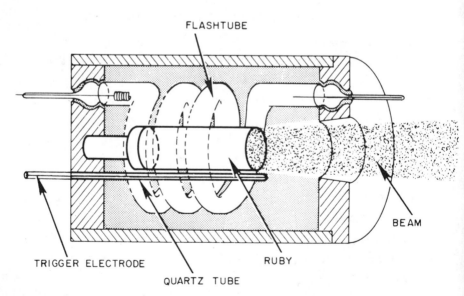

8. Cutaway sketch shows the parts of the first laser built by Dr. Maiman in 1960.

be wrong, but I had exhausted all the side tests. There was nothing left to do but turn it on and see.

"I checked everything over again and turned it on. There were no problems—it worked the first time."

Co-workers could not see a well-defined beam coming from the device and asked how Maiman knew it was working. He ran several calculations from the data presented by the detection equipment, all of which bore out the contention that a true laser beam was being emitted. The clincher was the curves shown by the spectrograph.

"Below the threshold level for laser activity, the curves for the two fluorescent lines were about equal, looking like the two humps on a camel's back. When the instruments indicated the apparatus was above the coherent light threshold, the R1 spectral line got very much narrower—the relative intensity ratio from line R2 to R1 went from roughly 1–1 to 25–1." This was definite evidence of amplification.

Meanwhile, whcn the news of the Hughes development was released, other scientists worked to repeat the experiment. Bell Laboratories used a more precise ruby to begin with and achieved a bright spot immediately. "For a time," says Maiman, "they suggested they had a different device and tried to point this up by calling it an optical maser instead of a laser.

"However, we had gotten out accurate ruby in the interim and had established beyond doubt that our device was what we claimed it to be. We had not publicized this, because we didn't want to increase the already staggering number of inquiries being directed to us from all parts of the country and the world. We did not release our improved results until I gave a detailed paper to the

American Optical Society. After this, it was plain that the BTL work had simply duplicated that done at Hughes."

The laser now was accomplished fact. The revolution in light had begun.

CHAPTER II

3-D MIRACLE: HOLOGRAPHY

The three-dimensional movies described at the beginning of Chapter I are one possible product of a new technology called holography. Holography was known long before the laser was invented, but it took the laser to change it from a scientific curiosity to an exciting concept with many promising applications.

Though home 3-D movies are presently only in the early research stages, many uses for still holographic photography have already reached the practical stage. The equipment needed for this is too expensive at this writing for the amateur photographer, but it is not overly costly for quite a number of scientific and industrial uses. In many programs, for instance, the ability of holography to "freeze" action in full three dimensions permits gaining information that can't be obtained by any other means. The Volkswagen Company, for instance, greatly improved the fuel injection system of its new cars by studying holograms that showed exactly what happened to all the droplets of gasoline as they entered the combustion chamber from the injection nozzle.

Like the laser, holography is in its infancy—at least from a practical standpoint. But it has developed almost

9. *A three-dimensional "solid" figure seems to rest on the table behind a glass window, an image that rotates as the viewer moves his head from one side to the other. Actually, the figure is not solid at all, but a projection from the glass "window" which is a holographic plate. The image is gained from illumination of the plate by coherent light from the laser in the background.*

as rapidly as the coherent light technology that is so vital to its success. In fact, though lasers and holography really are different processes, they have progressed almost side by side since the early 1960s.

The man credited with the founding of modern holography is the Hungarian-born physicist Dennis Gabor. He suggested the possibility of three-dimensional holographic imaging in 1947 when he was a young scientist at the Imperial College of Science and Technology in London, England. Gabor was interested in getting better pictures of tiny objects being studied under a powerful electron microscope. Because such an instrument is used to examine extremely small specimens, it poses problems of getting everything in the field of view in focus. As anyone who has used an ordinary camera is aware, the closer to an object the lens must be placed, the narrower is the zone in which sharp images can be obtained. If sharpness of large objects is so difficult to obtain with an ordinary hand camera, it's easy to visualize how much harder it is to take good pictures of objects so tiny they can't be seen at all with the naked eye.

Gabor reasoned the answer might lie in finding a way of taking a picture without using lenses. He envisioned a method in which the picture would be taken of the light from a scene rather than the scene itself. In effect, he thought of storing light information in the form of a grid that would contain not only the properties in a two-dimensional flat plane but at points along an axis stretching out from the point of view.

The theories of Gabor were based on the fact that light is a form of electromagnetic radiation. As such, it travels through space in the form of waves. These waves ripple

out from the source much as wave fronts in water extend
out in concentric circles from the point of impact of a
thrown stone. The positions of these circles can be established in space, Gabor noted, if part of the same radiation wave is caused to pass through—or interfere—with
the original wave. The photographic system then takes a
picture of these interferences.

The device used to store the data usually is a photographic plate coated with a special light-sensitive emulsion
that is much like the coating used on regular films. Because the holographic plate is recording light interference
patterns, no lens is needed to focus the light from the
subject on the plate. After the plate has been chemically
processed the original image can be reconstructed by passing the proper kind of electromagnetic radiation through
the glass. Gabor called this plate a hologram, from Greek
words meaning "whole message" or "entire picture."

It should be noted that while Gabor's idea of using
light interference to make 3-D images was new, his work
drew on research in principles of light interference proposed almost 150 years earlier. The fact that optical interference takes place in nature was observed and analyzed in 1801 by British physicist Thomas Young. The
idea of using light interference to produce unusual images
in two dimensions was suggested by a German experimenter, William Zenker, in 1868. Some years afterward,
in 1891, a French physicist named Gabriel Lippmann
applied Zenker's theories to produce the world's first color
photographs.

Lippmann used a glass plate with a photographic emulsion on one side and a reflecting surface of mercury on the
other. The reflections from the mercury met—and formed

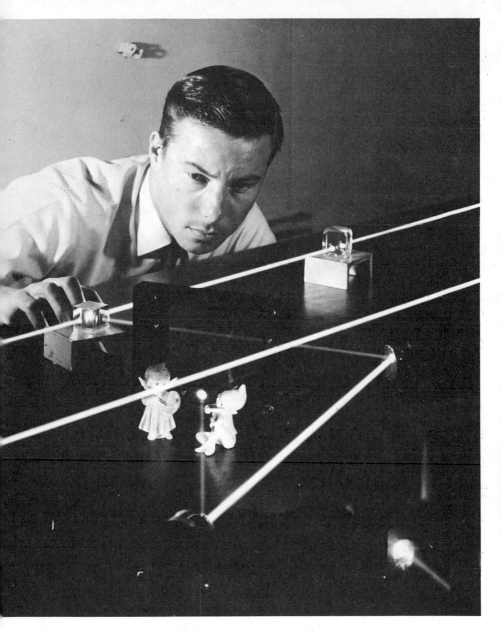

10. *Dr. Ronald Lundgren of Hughes Research Laboratories aligns mirrors and a laser beam to make a three-dimensional picture (that is, a hologram) of two pixielike figures without use of a lens.*

interference patterns—with the group of light waves just entering the emulsion. Acting somewhat like a prism, the interference waves created colored patterns when a light was beamed through the plate.

Gabor was able to demonstrate that his ideas really worked using ordinary white light. However, the images, while three dimensional, were anything but sharp. The problem was that the great range of frequencies in white light prevented the control of interference patterns essential for a well-reconstructed hologram. In addition, Gabor found the basic arrangement of an electron microscope is very difficult to adapt to achieving the interference radiation waves needed in his technique. As a result, after publishing a paper on his work, he turned his attention to other research.

In the 1950s, a few scientists tried to apply Gabor's principles in other research work. For instance, Drs. Hussein M. A. El-Sum, Paul Kirkpatrick, and Albert V. Baez (as a sidelight, Dr. Baez is the father of famous folk singer Joan Baez) of Stanford University used wave front reconstruction in X-ray microscopy. This instrument uses very high frequency waves—those known as X rays—to analyze specimens under the microscope.

In seeking new information about scientific processes and the nature of matter, researchers use many different instruments, because each device may provide some data not available from others. X-ray analysis is just one more way of piecing together the tremendous jigsaw puzzle of the world around us. Unfortunately, scientists have had even greater trouble taking good pictures of objects immersed in the beam of an X-ray microscope because focusing the instrument is even more difficult than for an electron microscope.

The idea of lensless photography was very appealing, and the Stanford experimenters studied ways of making holograms. They succeeded to some degree but, as with Gabor, the 3-D images were relatively crude and provided only a small amount of additional information compared to regular optical methods.

The main problem was the inefficient nature of the electromagnetic radiation used to expose the specimen for the hologram. Because this radiation was incoherent, it tended to cause unwanted extra interference patterns. Just like ghosts in a poorly tuned TV picture, these can cause a poorly defined, inaccurate image. Of course, special electronic filters can be used to minimize the frequency spread of the radiation, but these also weaken the effect of the beam. The drawbacks of incoherent radiation restricted Gabor's technique to specialized scientific research until Dr. Maiman invented the laser.

It didn't take very long after the news of Maiman's breakthrough had spread through the scientific community for some experts to begin thinking about using the laser to improve earlier scientific discoveries. Two scientists at the University of Michigan, Drs. Emmett N. Leith and Juris Upatnieks, realized the value of highly coherent light for wave reconstruction work. Gabor, El-Sum, et al., had to use all kinds of special equipment to gain the monochromatic, concentrated light needed for their holograms. The light gained in this way amounted to only a tiny fraction of the energy of the original beam.

As Leith and Upatnieks wrote in *Scientific American* (June 1965, p. 33), "The light produced by a laser . . . is

highly monochromatic and has extraordinary spatial coherence, thus making (earlier) wasteful processes . . .
unnecessary. The available light is several orders of mag-
nitude greater than the monochromatic, spatially coherent
light available from other sources. Hence the laser is
greatly superior to all other known sources for wave-front
reconstruction photography."

During 1962, Leith and Upatnieks developed their approach to holography and produced the first, relatively
crude holograms. They used the laser light in a different
way from Gabor's original interference studies. Their system splits the laser beam in two, with one portion providing an undisturbed "reference" beam. Gabor didn't do
this because it can't be accomplished with the radiation
available in an electron microscope. With a reference
beam, much more accurate interference patterns can be
obtained, resulting in considerable improvement in quality
over earlier 3-D pictures.

By the time Leith and Upatnieks began their work,
scientists and engineers throughout the world had developed many new kinds of lasers in addition to Maiman's
original system. These included lasers based on crystals other than ruby and lasers that used gas. The principle
of a gas laser is not much different from one using a
crystal. A volume of gas, such as helium, neon, or carbon
dioxide, is placed in a cavity with reflecting walls. Energy
is injected to pump the gas atoms or molecules to higher
energy levels, and the process of achieving a coherent
beam proceeds in the same way as for a ruby laser. For
some applications, one or the other of the gas systems
can have advantages over solid-state lasers, while for other
uses, the solid materials may be best.

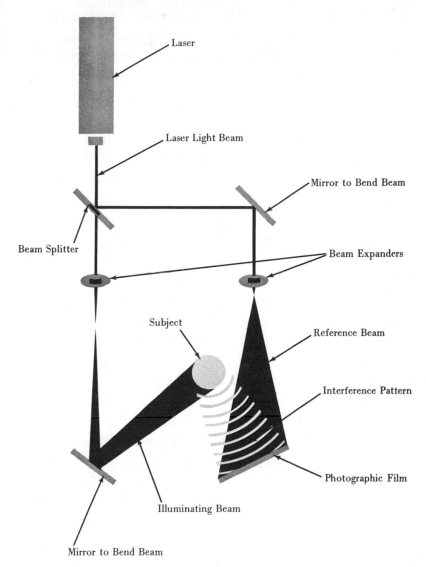

Laser

Laser Light Beam

Mirror to Bend Beam

Beam Splitter

Beam Expanders

Subject

Reference Beam

Interference Pattern

Photographic Film

Illuminating Beam

Mirror to Bend Beam

11. Arrangements of lasers and mirrors to take a hologram are shown in this diagram.

The Michigan scientists chose a continuous wave (CW) gas laser for their system. (Continuous wave means that the laser is stimulated by a constantly operating pumping device rather than a pulsed one as in the original laser. Put another way, a continuous wave laser operates continuously from the time it's turned on to when it's switched off. A pulsed laser, on the other hand, operates in short bursts.) They also added a mirror placed so that it reflected part of the laser beam at a preselected angle to the light arriving at the film from the subject.

To take a hologram with this system, the laser beam is split by a device at its output end so that part of it hits and is reflected from the subject, while part is reflected from the mirror. The beam from the mirror, the reference beam, comes back to the film plate with all its wave fronts at exactly the same angle and moving the same way. The beam from the object is still coherent—its waves all move in the same direction, but its wave fronts arrive at all kinds of angles. These various angles are the result of the infinite number of angles of the object from which the first beam has been reflected.

Meeting at the plate, the two beams interfere with each other either "constructively" or "destructively." Constructive interference means the waves tend to reinforce each other. In this case, the greater the reinforcement, the more the film is exposed, resulting in a darker image. In destructive interference, the reverse is true; the waves tend to cancel each other out.

These reinforcing or subtracting effects give information on one aspect of the subject being photographed— the light intensities in different sections of the subject. If this were all that holography provided, it would be little different from ordinary photography. A two-dimensional photograph taken with a regular camera derives its images from variations in the density of the light falling on the film.

The interaction between the beam from the subject, or the signal-bearing beam, and the reference beam provides the new data not found in regular photos. Where the signal-bearing beam meets a reference beam, the result is an interference pattern taking the form of a set of uniform, parallel set of fringes.

Leith and Upatnieks write that "the spacing of the fringes is related to the angle between the signal-bearing waves and the reference waves. At places where the signal-bearing waves make a large angle with the reference waves, the resulting fringe pattern is comparatively fine; at places where the waves meet at lesser angles, the fringe pattern is coarser. Therefore, the variations in the phase of the signal-bearing waves produce corresponding variations in the spacing of the fringes on the photographic record."

This fringe pattern, then, gives information on the location in space of the surfaces of the object that has been photographed. Given the light values of the subject and where these values are located with respect to the over-all surface allows reconstructing of a full-depth image.

After the film has been exposed, it is developed using chemical solutions in the same way any film is processed. The end result, though, has little resemblance to the usual photographic negative. If you hold the hologram up to the light, your first reaction is to throw it away. There is certainly nothing recognizable on the plate. The entire surface has a gray appearance with what look like blurry scratches that don't seem to follow any particular pattern.

In most cases, you can make out rippling concentric lines that intersect here and there. These lines look like the ripples in a pond caused by falling raindrops.

The first reaction is that the fringe patterns from these lines are the marks of the 3-D picture that will be recreated when a laser beam is directed through the plate. But this would be wrong. Actually, these faintly visible circles are caused by interference with the light by dust particles suspended in the air or by such things as non-uniformities in the film or flaws in the laser optics. The actual hologram takes the form of a fringe pattern in the emulsion so fine that it cannot be seen with the naked eye. Though it's hard to believe, when a laser beam shines through the plate, it only reconstructs the wave front in the microscopic pattern. None of the visible details from dust or optical flaws shows up in the playback image.

The method of reconstructing a hologram, as has been indicated, is essentially the reverse of making it, except that no mirror is needed. To reconstruct the same size image as the original, a laser with exactly the same properties as the one used to make the hologram is used. When the laser beam shines through the hologram, it constructs two images, a "real" one and a "virtual" one. The viewer can see either one of these, depending on the direction he looks at the hologram. If he looks up at the plate at the same angle the reference beam originally made with the signal-bearing beam, he sees the virtual image. This image seems to be the same distance behind the hologram that the original subject was in front of the photographic plate.

If the viewer looks down at the hologram at the same angle the original signal-bearing beam made with the reference beam, he sees the real image. This image seems

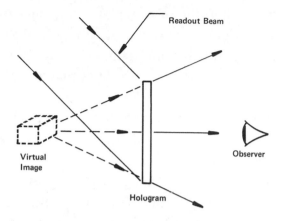

a) Viewing the Virtual Image of a Transmission Hologram

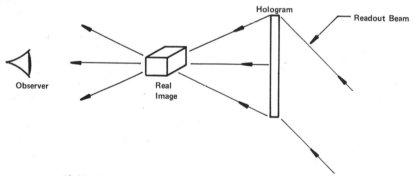

b) Viewing the Real Image of a Transmission Hologram

12. Depending on the way in which a hologram is illuminated by a light beam, the three-dimensional image can appear to hang in space behind the hologram (virtual image) or in front of the hologram (real image).

to float in space in front of the plate the same distance from it as the original solid object. In either case, the object is amazingly lifelike and solid-looking. This seems true until you pass your hand into the scene and find you are moving it through thin air.

Except for the proof that the holographic picture is only a light pattern and not the original subject, all else about it can appear as real as could be. You walk around the picture and its features change just as they would in an actual scene. Moving to one side, you see parts of the object come into view that weren't visible from the front. If there originally was a second object behind the front one that was hidden when viewed from the front, this object comes into view as you change position to look "behind" the front object. If you move backward or forward, the relative dimensions of the items in the scene change as they would in the real world.

One reason for calling the image in front of the hologram a real image, apart from the fact that its location is the same as the original subject, is that it can easily be copied. A regular two dimensional photograph of this image can be made without requiring a camera. This is done just by placing a film in the real image position and briefly exposing it. When the plate is developed, the result is a picture of the image.

A completed hologram has some unusual properties apart from the fact that it contains a three-dimensional image. Some of these would be hard to believe if it weren't for the fact that they can be proven by actual demonstration. For instance, each part of the hologram can reproduce the entire image. Thus you can take the finished hologram, cut it up into several pieces, shine a laser through each piece in turn, and see the same picture you previously could see from the original uncut hologram.

The reason for this, Leith and Upatnieks state, is that each point on the hologram receives light from all parts of the subject. Consequently, even the smallest fragment of hologram contains all the information needed for a complete picture. Theoretically, then, you could easily produce as many holograms of one subject as you want. However, there is a practical limit. The resolution—or sharpness—of the image is related to the light that comes through the plate. Thus each smaller piece of hologram will produce a fuzzier image until the point is reached at which too much detail is lost to make the picture worthwhile.

Another unusual feature of holography is that no negatives are produced. The hologram would normally be considered a negative because it is exposed and processed as a regular piece of film.* As anyone familiar with photography knows, when a piece of film taken in a normal camera is developed, the result is an image where all the light areas appear dark and vice versa. If you place the normal film negative in a projector and shine it on the wall, you still see a negative. With a hologram, when you shine a laser beam through it no negative appears—the subject looks as it did when it was first photographed. It is possible to make a contact print of the hologram, Leith and Upatnieks point out, that appears to have the properties of a negative in the same sense that dark areas seem light and light areas dark. But when a laser illumi-

---

* It should be noted that while most holograms to date have been made using photographic methods, there are a number of other ways of making holograms.

nates the copy, the image is a positive, as was the image from the original hologram.

In time, properties like these will probably be put to special use by scientists and engineers. If nothing else, it indicates ways in which holography is simpler than conventional photography even though setting up lasers and mirrors makes the method of today more complicated for the average person. Obviously, it is pretty hard to lose a picture through damage to the plate—if part of it is destroyed, you can just set up the remaining piece and get almost as good a picture as before. And someday, when simple home holographic equipment is available, it should be much easier to make on-the-spot copies for friends and relatives than with, say, today's Polaroid camera.

Making copies of holograms will probably be an important step, it should be noted, in home displays. The reason is the nature of the "real" versus the "virtual" image mentioned above. The virtual image, like the image in a regular mirror, seems to be behind the viewing surface. You have to look "into" the hologram to see the picture. For a home display or, say, some kind of promotion or training display, this limits the number of people that can see the picture at one time. The real image, which appears to be located in front of the screen, solves the problem. With the real image, people can see it from all sides and even walk into the picture.

The problem is that an original "real" image, while not looking like a negative, is an opposite of a kind. That is, when projected it is reversed. It is reversed in two ways— both in direction and in its three-dimensional properties. From a 3-D standpoint, the image is literally inside out.

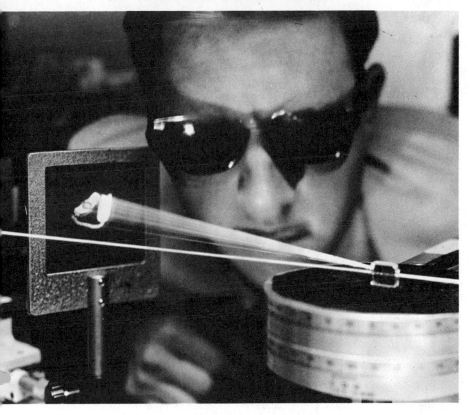

13. Image from a lithium niobate crystal is reconstructed with laser light on the screen in the background. This small crystal, developed at Bell Telephone Laboratories, can hold up to 1000 separate holograms. Each different hologram can be "read out" by rotating the crystal slightly in relation to the coherent light beam.

The answer is to make a copy of the first hologram. When this second hologram is projected, the real image presents the scene, floating in mid-air, as it was originally photographed.

The nature of holography, as the foregoing indicates,

allows the packing of a great deal of information into a small amount of space. Almost from the start, holographic experts discovered that not just one, but several different holographic pictures could be stored in a single, thin film emulsion. By increasing the depth of the sensitive layer, a great many different images can be stored and each one called up separately from the others.

This is done by changing the frequency of the light beam used to make each image. Thus each image will be sensitive only to a particular type of light beam. If a beam of one frequency is directed at the completed plate, one image will be reconstructed, and if this beam is removed and one of another frequency substituted, a different picture will appear. This process is similar to the one used in radio sets. In a radio, each station broadcasts over a certain frequency that is detected by a tuner that can be set for a range of different frequencies.

The fact that many different images can be stored in one hologram is the basis for several of the most promising development programs for the process. A great deal of work has been devoted to new kinds of computer memories. Using light patterns of different coherent frequencies to store information for later use by the computer may be the best way to build small, compact memories with tremendous storage capacity.

Of more direct interest to the average person is the possibility of storing entire books in tiny holographic cubes. Thus the library of the future may have many of its reference works stored in arrays of tiny blocks, providing tremendous savings in storage space. Because direct copies can be made of hologram images, the copying machine of tomorrow may be able to reproduce entire books in the

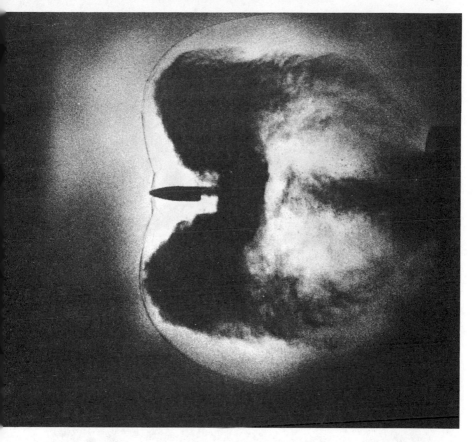

14. A single exposure hologram spectacularly freezes a bullet from an M-16 rifle in flight, millionths of a second after the bullet leaves the gun barrel. If seen as a full hologram, the picture would show the position of the bullet and air shock waves in three dimensions.

time it takes to copy one page with a Xerox copier today. Laboratory samples of hologram book storage have been made, but it will take many more years of research and development before this method becomes generally available.

The most widespread application of multiple holograms has been in time-lapse photography. Scientists and engineers working in many different fields have applied this

15. Holographic patterns are used in science and industry to study the effects of outside forces on objects. This TRW Systems holographic interferogram shows the vibratory motion induced in jet engine turbine blades when the blades are hit with a hammer. The first laser pulse was made one millionth of a second after hammer impact and the second 0.025 second later.

method to gain important new information on changes in complex systems. Experimenters at Bell Telephone Laboratories, for instance, used time-lapse holograms to detect the very tiny changes in the structure of a solid-state material (caused by variations in internal temperature) when an electric current was applied. Medical and biological experts have used the technique to study changes in human or animal tissue under different conditions.

Another group at TRW Systems, Redondo Beach, California, has taken extremely high-speed time-lapse holograms that have been termed "spectacular" by people who have seen them. Among the subjects photographed were a complete set of holograms of a bullet in flight, showing the shock-wave patterns at intervals of millionths of a second. In another series of holograms, the experimenters obtained three-dimensional images of the effect on air caused by the movement of a tiny fruit fly's wings.

Though the best way to project a hologram is with a laser, standard light sources can be used to produce a 3-D picture. One method is to use a small, high-intensity lamp such as that used in home movie or slide projectors. This lamp must be placed in a housing allowing only a pinhole-sized opening. The light coming through the pinhole is much closer to the coherent state than the original light put out by the lamp. Next a color filter is placed over the pinhole to make the tiny beam as nearly monochromatic as possible. When this light shines through a hologram, the viewer does see a striking 3-D image, though it is a little fuzzy and much of the original detail disappears. This kind of system could be easily assembled by a home craftsman. More sophisticated systems are being devised

by engineers that may someday permit good—if not per-
fect—home 3-D viewers without the need for a laser.

The reader might wonder how color holograms can result from pictures taken in monochromatic light. The answer is, they don't; the holograms discussed thus far are
single-color pictures. The method of making a color hologram, as might be expected, requires using three separate
laser beams, one red, one blue, and one green. The color
process makes use of the just mentioned principle of storing a number of different holograms in one emulsion. The
lasers are arranged to illuminate the subject from different
angles and, since the primary colors are at different wavelengths, three separate images are recorded on the film.

The color hologram thus can produce three different
images if three light beams of different frequencies are
beamed through it in succession. An image can be produced in full color by using the three different lasers simultaneously. However, white light can be used for full-
color reproduction because it naturally contains all the
colors of the spectrum.

Just as work with stimulated emission of radiation in
the microwave part of the electromagnetic spectrum led in
time to the use of these principles at the frequencies of
light, holographic principles have been extended in other
directions. In recent years, experimenters have developed
hologram-laser systems that work with sound waves rather
than light. This new discipline is called sonoptography or
acoustic holography.

Some of the pioneering work in acoustic holography
took place at McDonnell Douglas Corporation's Research
Laboratories in Huntington Beach, California, in the late
1960s. Starting in 1967, a group headed by Dr. Alexander

F. Metherell became interested in developing 3-D images from sound as part of a research program on underwater detection systems.

Almost all devices used to send signals through the water depend on sound waves. The reason is that sound is the only form of energy that penetrates water to any extent. A sound wave can travel for hundreds of miles underwater and still remain reasonably clear, whereas radio or light waves "smear out" and disappear in anywhere from a few feet to several tens of miles. Thus scientists are always looking for better ways of using sound for such things as underwater surveys, monitoring of hostile submarines, communications, etc. Metherell's group decided the use of sound-induced holograms could provide a breakthrough of unmatched dimensions for such work. With a 3-D imaging system, operators on ships or subs could tell at a glance whether the signals they were receiving came from an enemy sub, a whale, or just a mass of seaweed. The 3-D system could also be much more effective than radar in preventing accidents at sea.

By the end of 1967, Metherell and his co-workers had devised systems that proved acoustic holography could be done. The basic system used an electromechanical device called a transducer to send out a series of sound waves. Instead of using light for a reference beam, an electrical signal was added to gain the third dimension. After the sound waves reflect back from an object, they pass through a laser beam and the signals resulting from this interaction are detected by the system's electronics and presented on a TV-type screen. The acoustic hologram is obtained by taking a photograph of the pattern on the screen. The photographic plate is then developed and the

3-D image reconstructed by shining a laser beam through it.

The science of sound holography is still only in its be-

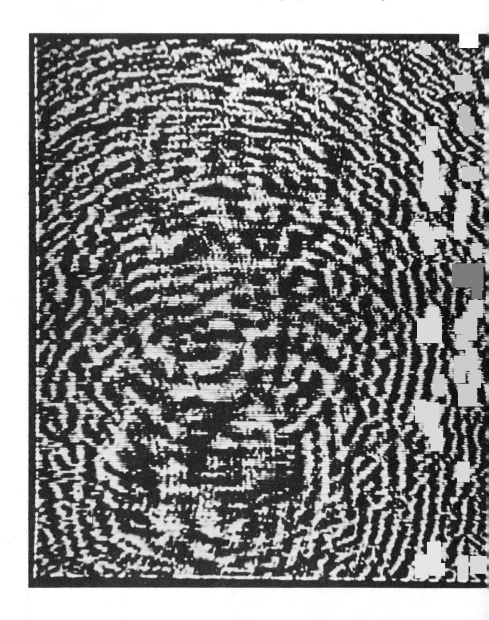

ginning stages. Already many variations of its principles have been studied for possible applications in many ways besides detecting underwater vehicles. Medical experimenters, for instance, believe sound holography may eventually prove as important as X rays in fighting illness. In crude fashion, they have already shown that proper focusing and later reconstruction of sound waves beamed at

16. & 17. Acoustic holography combines principles of sound waves with coherent light to make special kinds of holograms. Picture at left shows a typical acoustic hologram as it appears to the naked eye. After this plate is illuminated with laser light, it can be seen that it contains the letters ARL.

living tissue can present a 3-D image of internal systems. Engineers are looking at other sound holograms to provide 3-D pictures of the internal structure of all kinds of devices. From this data, they can detect dangerous flaws in materials or assemblies so that defective parts can be discarded.

All in all, laser-based holography will play an increasingly important role in years to come, not only in entertaining man, but also by protecting him and giving new insight into the wonders of the universe.

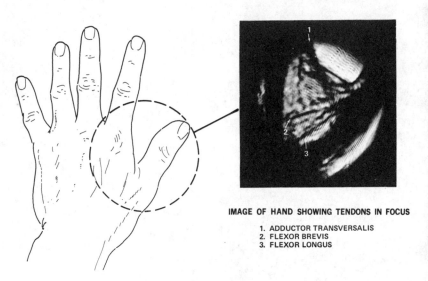

IMAGE OF HAND SHOWING TENDONS IN FOCUS

1. ADDUCTOR TRANSVERSALIS
2. FLEXOR BREVIS
3. FLEXOR LONGUS

18. Major use of acoustic holography promises to be in medicine. Picture at right shows how an acoustic hologram can provide images of soft tissues inside a human hand.

18A. *Art in industry—sequence photographs of an eight-inch-diameter by 0.062-inch-thick aluminum plate undergoing holographic stress studies show an intriguing variety of patterns of hologram interference fringes. The varied stress patterns captured in the holograms were produced by applying changing rates of vibration from 1685 Hertz up to 7340 Hertz (the Hertz, or Hz, symbol stands for cycles per second).*

CHAPTER III

ONE BREAKTHROUGH AFTER ANOTHER

The revolution in light, like the industrial revolution, has turned out to be made of many mini-revolutions. Almost yearly, since Dr. Maiman's ruby laser, new breakthroughs have been reported by scientists of the world, extending the principles of light amplification by stimulated emission of radiation over an ever wider span of the electromagnetic spectrum. These breakthroughs embrace thousands of new kinds of lasing materials used in all kinds of new ways.

Side by side with reports of development of many new crystals for devices based on Maiman's work came announcements of other, different systems. These lasers were based on other classes of materials and a variety of pumping methods. In the second half of 1960, several new crystals were used by M. J. Stevenson and P. P. Sirokin of IBM. These were uranium-doped and samarium-doped calcium fluoride excited by essentially the same pumping system used by Maiman. In February 1961, the first operating gas laser, an electrically excited helium-neon device, was reported by Ali Javan, W. R. Bennett, and D. R. Herriott. In November 1962, experimenters at three different laboratories, Lincoln Laboratory of MIT, IBM, and General Electric, independently announced success with semiconductor lasing material. A month later, Hughes reported

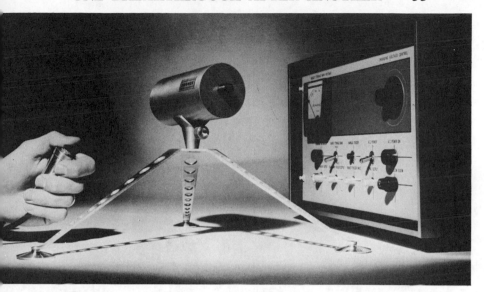

19. Only a few years after Dr. Maiman built the first laser, small one-pound laser-light producers, such as this one, were being offered commercially by Hughes Aircraft.

still another first—the production of coherent light from liquids. In 1964, Bell Telephone Laboratories proudly reported the first carbon dioxide laser, a special category of gas lasers that promised power output many times that of the best devices developed earlier.

As we shall see, all of these advances pioneered new frontiers for laser technology. Their extensions of the operating range of coherent light systems eventually will dramatically increase the impact of the laser on human activities. However, the breakthrough that may, in time, have the greatest effect of all did not occur until the 1960s almost had ended. This was the almost simultaneous demonstration at Cornell University in New York and

Aerospace Corporation in California of the first all-chemical laser.

After the first brief reports of these tests were published in the *International Journal of Chemical Kinetics,* the journal's editor, Dr. Sidney Benson, hailed it as "one of the most significant scientific advances in the past decade." Benson, a nationally known researcher in thermochemistry and chemical kinetics at Stanford Research

20. Gas laser operating in the laboratory of TRW Systems, Redondo Beach, California, lights up the room with an eerie glow reminiscent of science fiction films.

Institute, pointed out that "scientists have been searching for years for an all-chemical laser as the only answer to the problem of generating large amounts of energy in the form of coherent light. The potential applications for such a laser are limitless."

Though Benson's predictions may well come true, the earlier discoveries undoubtedly will lead to a great many practical applications long before chemical lasers move out of the laboratory. Because each system has both advantages and disadvantages, as the ensuing pages will indicate, it seems likely that each class of laser will find its own special niche.

Gas laser technology derives from the discovery that atoms of certain gases can be raised to the higher levels of energy needed for lasing if a strong electric current is passed through the gas. Most of the gases that can be readily excited in this way belong to the group called the "noble" gases. Since the first gas laser of Javan and his co-workers, many operating lasers have been built using a noble gas alone or in combination with other gases, such as helium-neon, argon, krypton, xenon. However, lasers can be made using other than noble gases; most of this work to date has been concentrated on nitrogen or the special case of carbon dioxide-nitrogen mixture.

The fact that electricity is used instead of light for pumping is one feature that makes gas lasers simpler than other types. The gas is excited in a tube or other container having mirrors at each end. As with the ruby laser, the coherent beam bounces back and forth from one mirror to the other through the gas, building up energy until it reaches the desired concentration for emission as a laser beam through the output end.

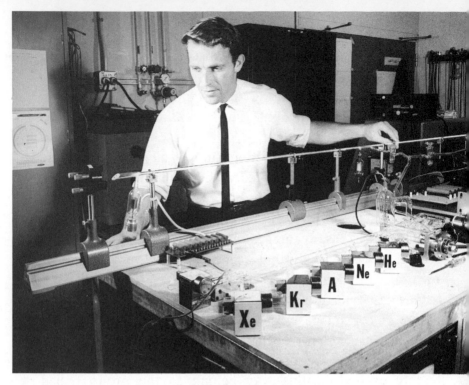

21. A scientist at Hughes Research Laboratories fills the long tube of an experimental gas laser with xenon, one of the noble gases.

The many kinds of gas mixtures and instrument arrangements that can be used permit choosing any of several hundred frequencies for the coherent beam produced by this laser system. Most gas lasers have the advantage of continuous operation. That is, the electric current can run continuously and the gas be recirculated so that laser action keeps going as long as the device is turned on. The typical gas laser is preferable where very high power is desired in the visible range, because solid materials are hard to operate at such powers. Gases are not used in very high energy pulsed systems because the gas density doesn't allow high storage capability, and the time that the atoms in a gas can hold stored energy is much less than excited atoms in a solid.

In general, though, noble gas lasers are probably the most used today. In almost every laboratory, as Richard Einhorn stresses in *Electronic Design,* one can walk in and "see the familiar glow of a helium-neon laser emitting at 0.6328 micron. This is no accident: it's the simplest and least expensive laser to build. All one really needs is a Pyrex glass tube with Brewster-angle windows (fastened

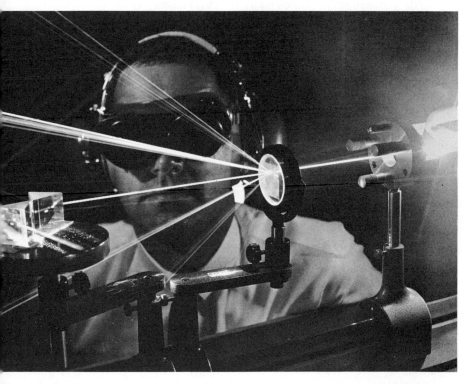

22. Rays from an argon gas laser are sent off in many directions in tests of a possible link in a future space communication system.

with epoxy cement) onto the ends, a pair of electrodes, a couple of high-quality dielectrically coated mirrors, a power supply, and a mount. It doesn't even need external cooling. Alignment tolerances on the mirrors are less critical than those of any other types."

The over-all simplicity of noble gas type lasers also makes them candidates for many future home or commercial uses. As we will see in Chapter IV, gas lasers may play a prominent role in future communication systems. Today, lasers of this family can be bought for well under $200, and some laser engineers say it may soon be possible to sell some designs for under $50.

But noble gas lasers have some serious shortcomings apart from being restricted to low power uses. The most serious of these is very poor efficiency. In fact, most of this class of lasers have the lowest efficiency of all laser designs. The best one demonstrated is an argon gas unit with an efficiency of 0.1 per cent. In other words, to gain one watt of power in the form of coherent light, 1000 watts of electricity are required. For some of these lasers, 4000 or 5000 watts may be needed for one watt output.

Maiman's original ruby laser had an efficiency of less than 1 per cent. Since then, better laser crystals have come into use. Much of the improved materials are based on the family of elements called rare earths. Rare earths include yttrium, neodymium, samarium, etc. (In truth, some of these elements really aren't that rare today.) Among the solid crystals used in many lasers are such exotic-sounding crystals as yttrium-aluminum-garnet containing ions of the rare earth neodymium (nicknamed YAG); calcium fluorapatite (called FAP); and plain optical-quality glass containing rare earth ions.

These optically pumped systems can provide much higher powers—thousands of watts in pulsed operation compared to less than one watt for most gas lasers. Lasers using either glass or ruby crystals can also be operated in a way known as Q-switching to provide light beams with fantastic amounts of instantaneous peak power— several billion watts at a time. However, it should be stressed that these power levels can only be made for very short times—measured in fractions of a second.

Q-switching isn't really as exotic as it sounds. Simply speaking, it's a technique for storing up a lot of excited atoms or molecules, then letting everything go in one burst, the same thing that happens if a dam holding back a river or lake is suddenly opened. Here's how Q-switching is accomplished: the laser material is excited until it reaches the right concentration of stimulated atoms for a coherent beam. The process is held up, though, by a special shutter that closes off the laser rod from one of the end mirrors. More and more excited atoms pile up and thus, when the shutter is opened, the coherent light pours out at much higher intensity that it would normally have.

The development of a laser based on a semiconductor material, the family of materials that led to the transistor radio and the well-advertised solid-state TV sets, was described by Dr. Guy Suits, General Electric's director of research, as "a major milestone in laser research." The pioneering work that helped clear the way for the semiconductor laser was performed at Lincoln Laboratory. Scientists at this government-supported facility developed the first solid state incoherent diode and could have made the first coherent version, except that the research team did not immediately realize how close they were to this breakthrough. When they did, a group headed by Dr. T. M. Quist set to work on it and succeeded almost simultaneously with teams at GE and IBM. The GE team that accomplished this was headed by Dr. Robert N. Hall of the Schenectady, New York, laboratory. His group first reported its pulsed semiconductor laser on November 1, 1962.

The material used for this laser is called gallium arsenide. The coherent light was generated by passing an electric current through a specially shaped piece of gallium arsenide no longer than the head of an ordinary pin. This piece actually consisted of two sections of gallium arsenide, each having a slightly different arrangement of the electrons in the gallium arsenide atoms. Semiconductor action is based on the movement of electrons from one section to the other, across the thin junction between them, when an electric current is applied.

Scientists finally achieved this by applying very concentrated electric current to gallium arsenide material. In GE's successful laser, every square centimeter of the material was subjected to a current of 20,000 amperes. The mirror effect needed for laser action was achieved by polishing highly the front and back surfaces of the semiconductor and making these two surfaces almost perfectly parallel. (Later it was found that the reflecting effects could be gained more easily by carefully cleaving the semiconductor material along certain planes that provided extremely smooth surfaces.)

After the first beam of coherent radiation had been detected coming from the gallium arsenide junction, Dr. Suits stressed the meaning of the accomplishment. "Dr. Hall and his colleagues have achieved the simplest, most

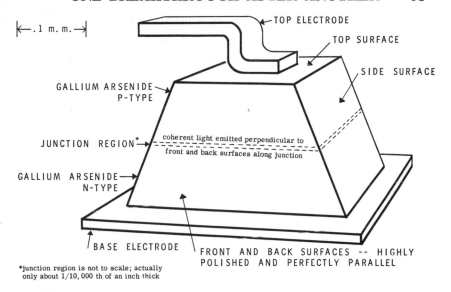

23. This diagram (many times actual size) shows the main parts of the semiconductor laser developed by General Electric in 1962.

compact, and most direct method yet discovered for producing coherent light. This transistor-sized device is by far the most efficient laser ever developed."

Theoretically, a laser based on gallium arsenide can be 100 per cent efficient. Before new lasers were developed, many studies had been made of the non-coherent light that can be obtained from a gallium arsenide electronic device. These showed that close to 100 per cent of the applied electrical energy can be transformed into infrared light. It's not easy to do this in coherent ranges, but early experiments showed at least half of all the light generated with the new system was coherent when cooled to 20° above absolute zero.

Almost the same day GE and Lincoln Labs reported

their semiconductor lasers, IBM reported that a group headed by Dr. M. I. Nathan had done the same thing. The IBM system achieved a coherent output for a smaller current density—10,000 amperes per square centimeter. The IBM laser, like GE's, only operated in short pulses because of the huge current inputs. Within ten days, however, IBM announced a giant step forward. By using gallium arsenide with different kinds of additional substances, its scientists were able to gain a coherent output for only 100 amperes/square centimeter. Under refrigerated conditions, the laser was able to operate continuously as long as electric current was applied.

Despite all this, the semiconductor laser had major limitations. The most important was the requirement of extreme refrigeration. The semiconductor had to be cooled by baths of liquid helium or liquid nitrogen. The temperatures needed to keep these materials in liquid, rather than gaseous, form is 269° C. below zero for helium and −196° C. for nitrogen. These very low temperature fluids were needed to remove the great amounts of heat caused by the concentration of electric energy needed to make the semiconductor work as a laser.

The efficiency of the semiconductor laser has improved steadily since its invention. Using new, improved materials, laser experts have built devices that convert 70 per cent of the electrical energy into coherent radiation. However, because of the tiny size of the semiconductor, the amount of power gained so far is not very large. The main drawback for many applications, though, has remained refrigeration. In 1962, IBM and GE scientists believed ways would quickly be found to operate these lasers at higher and higher temperatures.

By the end of the 1960s, tiny semiconductor lasers had been developed that could work at or near room temperature. Unfortunately, the heat generated by the electric current passing through the very small active area of the laser was still too high. The devices worked, but could only be operated for very small periods of time—on the order of 0.0001 second. At the start of the 1970s, the best semiconductor lasers still needed cooling jackets of helium or nitrogen.

Because of the promise of these compact lasers, experts at hundreds of laboratories concentrated on finding some combination of electronic materials and circuitry that might remove the roadblock. Each group pored over the properties of hundreds of materials and assembled minute bits of different substances in an almost endless series of patterns. Finally, in late 1970, Bell Telephone Laboratories announced that its experts had developed a semiconductor laser that could operate continuously at room temperature. BTL estimated the new laser could operate for up to a million hours without failure.

When reporters were shown the new system by the inventors, Izuo Kayashi and Morton B. Panish, of BTL's Murray Hill, New Jersey, laboratory, they had to strain their eyes to see anything at all. The specially designed semiconductor structure was a sandwich of several materials, but it was so small its entire length was about the width of Lincoln's lips on a one-cent coin. The structure consisted of four alternating layers of gallium arsenide and gallium aluminum arsenide. The layers contained small amounts of the elements tin, silicon, zinc, and germanium. The complete laser section was smaller than a grain of sand.

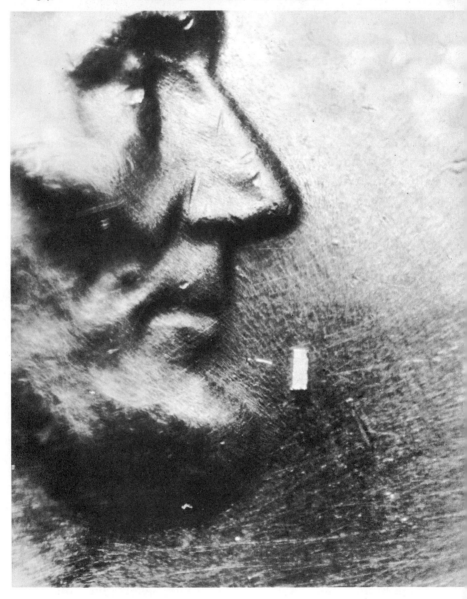

24. *The little white block contrasted against the image on a Lincoln penny is the tiny solid-state laser, announced by Bell Telephone Laboratories in August 1970, that can work at room temperature.*

25. *Izuo Kayashi of Bell Telephone Laboratories points to the location of the microminiature room temperature semiconductor laser announced in 1970.*

While this advance pointed toward incorporation of lasers in all kinds of equipment of the future, experts knew there was still much work required before this happened. The new device demonstrated that room temperature semiconductor lasers were a reality, but it had power outputs of only a fraction of a watt and an efficiency of only 1.5 to 2 per cent.

Within a month after the first semiconductor lasers were reported, the first liquid lasers were unveiled. Hughes Research Laboratory operated the first device with the organic liquid nitrobenzene in July 1962. By December,

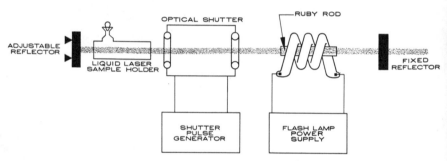

26. Main parts of a liquid laser are indicated in this diagram.

when its researchers announced their successes, seven fluids had been found that could produce coherent light. Many of these are commonly used household products, such things as cleaning fluids, antiseptics and saccharin. Besides nitrobenzene, the fluids are: benzene, toluene (the source of the artificial sweetener, saccharin), 1- bromonaphthalene, pyridine, cyclohexane, and deuterated benzene.

Liquid lasers, Dr. George Smith pointed out, applied a

phenomenon long known to scientists but never before used in lasers, the Raman effect. This effect occurs in certain substances when a beam of light is directed at their molecules and is scattered. It might normally be concluded that the scattered light would have the same properties as the original incoming light. In fact, experiments showed the outgoing light has different energy and wavelength. The difference, physicists determined, was caused by the transfer of some of the energy of the incoming light to the molecules, energy that caused these bits of matter to vibrate.

The relation of the Raman effect to making a coherent liquid laser was discovered accidentally. Dr. E. J. Woodbury was running tests of a Q-switched laser when he detected an additional wavelength in his data that didn't seem to fit in with expected results. After rechecking his experiment, he traced this wavelength to a liquid called nitrobenzene present in the apparatus called a Kerr cell used in performing Q-switching.

He discussed it with his associates. Two of them, Dr. Giesela Eckhardt and Dr. Robert Hellworth, correctly identified the phenomenon as a Raman effect and ran tests that proved it. Calculations from these tests indicated the Raman effect might be used to excite liquid molecules to the energy levels needed for coherent radiation. There was one major problem: a very strong light input was required to start laser action in the liquid. The solution turned out to be fairly simple. "What provides an intense beam of light?" Hughes scientists asked themselves. Obviously the answer is a laser. So the Hughes team used a high power, short pulse (that is, Q-switched) ruby laser to start the liquid laser operating.

27. *Dr. F. J. McClung of Hughes Research Laboratories pours a special liquid into the operating section of the new liquid laser system developed by Hughes in 1963. Exciting of the liquid atoms to lasing energy levels is achieved by beam from a ruby laser at the extreme right of the instrument.*

The Hughes system proved the possibility of liquid lasers, but it was not an optimum approach, because it required the use of two lasers instead of one. As the 1960s progressed, however, methods were developed to pump liquid to excited levels using more direct energy inputs. This greatly increased the outlook for practical uses of such lasers.

Liquid lasers offered a number of new advantages. The liquids are available for only a few dollars a bottle. This is a major saving over solid-state materials, for example, which must be made by expensive methods. For instance, the crystals used in solid lasers must be grown, atom by atom, in special machines and then must be very carefully cut and polished to close tolerances. The liquid not only is less costly, but it can be readied in a matter of minutes when it is wanted. Then, if it's desired to have a bigger laser for more extensive lasing action, all you have to do is take a bigger laser tube and pour in more of the liquid. The solid obviously is a fixed quantity.

The problems of getting rid of heat generated in the laser material also is relatively simple with liquids. Cooling is gained by circulating some of the liquid around the device. Liquids also offer a simple method of tuning from one frequency to another. This can be done just by switching from one kind of liquid to another.

With all these pluses, liquids still aren't a cure-all. They have the disadvantage of being relatively bulky compared to solids and gases for low power use. In addition, the efficiency of the most common liquids isn't too high. Much better performance has been gained with some unusual kinds of liquids, but these are not the easiest materials to operate with.

One of the most promising liquid lasers developed in recent years, for example, was one that used an inorganic liquid called selenium oxychloride in which a small amount of the rare earth metal neodymium was dissolved. A laser using this combination has been studied by General Telephone & Electronics Corporation's Dr. Alex Lempicki. The device produced a coherent beam with properties almost the same as provided by a good solid laser.

But selenium oxychloride is a corrosive solvent. This means it can attack and dissolve many materials. Special efforts had to be made, therefore, to develop a housing for the liquid that would not be eaten away. Another drawback of the liquid is its poisonous nature. As Dr. Lempicki reported in *Electronic Design,* "One drop is enough to kill a mouse, and it wouldn't take too many to kill a man." Later in his work, Lempicki substituted a liquid called phosphorus oxychloride, which is much less dangerous than the selenium liquid. But this too is a solvent with all the design problems this brings up.

Nonetheless, GTE and other research groups continue to work on liquid lasers because they can be made to operate at just the right frequencies for some kinds of communications systems. These lasers also can turn out, continuously, beams with powers considerably higher than most other lasers.

The next major breakthrough after the liquid laser was the carbon dioxide laser. The first demonstration that this common gas could be excited by an electric current to coherent radiation levels was made by Bell Telephone Laboratories in mid 1964. The excitement this created in the laser field was almost as great as the first ruby laser because the equations for a carbon dioxide

(CO_2) system indicated this could be a "brute force" laser. Put another way, the amount of energy promised by carbon dioxide lasers was far beyond the output of any system developed before it. Harnessing this energy potential, scientists knew, could provide such things as laser cutting tools that could cut thick steel sheets like butter or send signals over far greater distances through the atmosphere than other devices.

Equally important, studies showed a CO_2 laser could be very efficient while turning out hundreds or even thousands of watts. As much as 30 per cent of the electrical energy used to pump the gas system could be converted to coherent output.

An important feature of this gas is that it can lase alone or in combination with other gases, such as nitrogen or helium. Mixing these other gases into the carbon di-

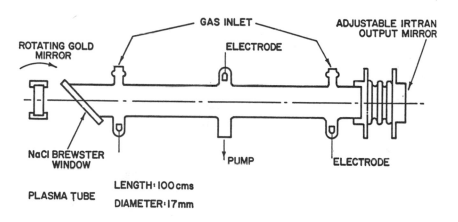

28. Diagram of a Q-switched carbon dioxide laser shows the close similarity of this laser to a neon tube. Note the Brewster window, a special arrangement for screening out selected wavelengths of laser light. The rotating mirror is used to control the build-up of coherent light atoms for the Q-switched effect described in this chapter.

oxide greatly improved its power output. Within a year after Patel of Bell Laboratories ran the first CO_2 laser, he was able to increase its power several hundred times (from 1 milliwatt to 10 watts) by adding nitrogen. In 1965, J. Dane Rigden and his co-workers at Perkin-Elmer Corporation, Norwalk, Connecticut, increased the power output ten times by adding helium. Since then, improvement of the design of the laser equipment and preparation of even better gas mixtures led to outputs approaching the 10,000 watt mark.

The CO_2 laser is considered as separate from other gas lasers for several reasons. For one thing, most conventional gas lasers are based on noble gases; for another, the properties of the CO_2 laser are very different from the noble gas systems. CO_2 lasers are even easier to build than helium-neon, argon, etc. The device looks a lot like a regular neon tube and, in fact, it is often made with the same electrical contacts and transformers used in the neon signs that shine on city streets at night.

There is no limit on the length of a carbon dioxide tube, which is one feature that allows development of CO_2 lasers with higher and higher powers. But this is also a disadvantage, because it can result in huge space requirements. Some of the most powerful CO_2 lasers built in the laboratory require enough space for an entire small apartment. To some extent, companies making lasers for industry have solved this by folding the tube that holds the excited gas mixture into a series of smaller sections. Thus a 100-foot-long tube can be compressed into ten sections of ten feet each. However, even the folded system takes a lot of space. Another drawback is that the stimulated gas mixture doesn't send out a beam in the visible

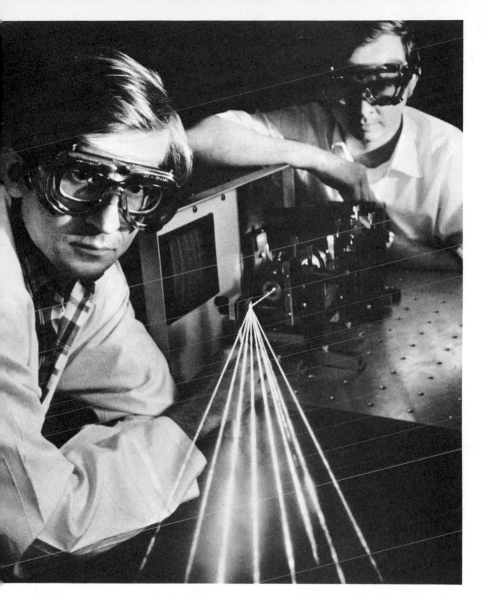

29. *One of the newest lasers is the Exciplex laser, developed at Bell Telephone Laboratories, which uses a special dye as the lasing material. Here Andrew Dienes (left) and Charles V. Shank, two of this laser's inventors, demonstrate that many different colored laser beams (each of the rays shown here is a different color), from near ultraviolet to yellow, can be gained from one dye material.*

range, but in the infrared part of the spectrum. This prevents using the beam for display systems, but it doesn't affect the promise of these lasers for communications.

All of the systems developed through the mid 1960s opened new doors for laser technology. But the more the boundaries of laser operation were extended, the more experimenters sought to push the limits out further. This was vital to development of practical laser systems, because many of the devices studied in the early years had little more than scientific potential. They could do many things that older devices such as radios or electric motors could do, but not in a way that gave them an economic edge over the older systems. Thus by the end of the 1960s, there were hundreds of very interesting uses for lasers, but none of these added up to mass production markets that could turn the laser industry into a major one employing tens of thousands of people.

Analyzing the technology in the mid 1960s, experts could see the limits of existing systems. Some devices provided low powers at low efficiency or very high power for very short periods of time. Others provided excellent efficiency, but with only limited power output. Still others had reasonably good power output and efficiency, but even then fell short of the performance that could be used for very large tasks. And all of the different families of lasers then in existence were further limited by the need for some outside system—light sources or electricity —to get laser action started.

One method that promised high efficiency, elimination of an outside pump, and very high energy beams, was to make an all-chemical laser. Scientists at many research facilities, government and private, began looking for systems based on chemicals alone. They reasoned that it might be possible to achieve laser action by a chemical reaction between the proper substances. After all, chemical reactions provide the light in a flame or the intense light of a welding torch; perhaps systems could be found to go one step further and produce coherent light.

Scientists and engineers in many parts of the United States began to analyze all kinds of chemical combinations. By 1968 some progress had been made. An all-chemical laser had not been invented, but some groups demonstrated chemically pumped lasers. These devices used the energy from chemical reactions to pump other substances to the higher energy states for lasing.

With each passing month, the knowledge about chemical laser requirements grew and rumors began to circulate in the scientific community that success might be near. In the spring of 1969, two groups, one in the eastern United States and one in the west, began to assemble special chambers, mirrors and high temperature heaters to prove out what seemed to be promising concepts. The eastern group at Cornell University's Laboratory of Plasma Studies, headed by T. A. Cool, R. A. Stephens, and T. J. Falk, planned to work with chemically excited carbon dioxide. The other group, at the Air Force-supported Aerospace Corporation, based its hopes on interactions between hydrogen, nitrogen, and fluorine.

Both groups worked independently, unaware they were in a race to complete the first all-chemical system. The painstaking process of carefully shaping each part and deciding on the proper arrangement of all the surface and attachments proceeded steadily at both institutions. By the end of April, both installations were ready for the

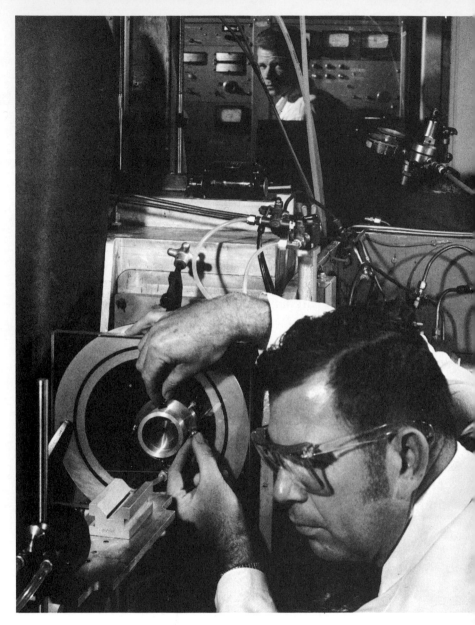

30. *Scientist at Aerospace Corporation adjusts the optics of the world's first successful chemical laser. Sometime in the future, descendants of this system may provide great amounts of pollution-free energy for many of man's requirements.*

first runs. By just a few days, the honor went to California. In early May, D. J. Spencer, T. A. Jacobs, H. Mirels, and R. W. Gross of the Aerophysics Department and the Aerodynamics and Propulsion Laboratory of Aerospace Corporation excitedly waited to open the valves to start three gases flowing into a chamber not much bigger than a small jet engine.

To some extent, the system resembled a rocket engine. Gases were heated at one end to very high temperature (by an arc heater), then allowed to expand suddenly through a nozzle just as the exhaust gas in a jet or rocket engine does. However, things changed from this point on. The rocket exhaust simply goes into the atmosphere, but the flow from the chemical laser travels past an optical cavity arranged with mirrors and polished walls in typical laser fashion.

The first requirement for the system to work was to have the gas jet travel at speeds above the speed of sound. The gas mixture chosen to do this consisted of nitrogen and sulfur tetrafluoride. The resulting supersonic flow was mainly composed of nitrogen with a small amount of the element fluorine in it. The fluorine was the most important part, though, because the goal was to cause a reaction between the fluorine and a stream of molecular hydrogen injected into the flow just before the optical cavity. The chemical interaction resulting from the formation of hydrogen fluoride, preliminary studies indicated, would raise the hydrogen fluoride molecules to the excited levels needed for laser action.

The Aerospace team determined all was in order and began the heating of the gases. With a roar, the mixture rushed through the nozzle, mixing with the hydrogen

31. Beam from world's first operational chemical laser at Aerospace Corporation is invisible to the human eye. However, its presence is demonstrated by fiery hole it cuts through a wood beam target.

as it went. The test lasted for only thirty seconds, but it was conclusive. A laser beam was detected coming from the optical cavity set at right angles to the flow. The beam was not very strong—only one watt, but the all-chemical laser was a reality.

Before the month was out, Cornell University had operated their apparatus. In their system, the first step was to cause a reaction, in a special borosilicate glass tube, of chlorine atoms and hydrogen iodide to form hydrogen chloride and iodine. The vibrational energy acquired by

the hydrogen chloride is used to excite carbon diox.
to the levels needed for lasing.

Before 1969 was over, chemical lasers were being operated at Aerospace, Cornell, and other laboratories with
outputs several thousand times that of the first small
attempts. Some of these systems eliminated the need for
an ouside heater. For instance, Aerospace ran experiments
in which a combination of hydrogen with fluorine provided the explosion needed for the supersonic flow.

As Dr. Sidney Benson points out, eventually it seems
possible an all-chemical laser may generate the extremely
short bursts of high energy needed to initiate atomic fusion.
"Such a feat," Benson underlines, "could make obsolete
all existing types of electrical energy generation, doing
away with the need for hydroelectric dams and the burning of fossil fuels to turn electrical generators.

"The potential applications for such a laser are limitless. It is possible they could be used for drilling tun-
nels through solid rock or for precision machining of
large metal, plastic, or ceramic objects. I can even
visualize them being used for rapid cutting of large trees
in forestry operations, or perhaps for demolition of large
buildings."

Not all scientists were as optimistic as Benson. They
generally agreed the chemical laser had fantastic potential.
But they also knew it would require many years, possibly
many decades, of intensive study and experiment to develop the method from its first halting steps to one of
mankind's most significant aids.

CHAPTER IV

LASERS COME OF AGE

The decade of the 1960s might be called the infancy of the laser. Most of the efforts of these years consisted of theoretical and experimental work that expanded scientific knowledge of the nature of coherent light. Yet, as the preceding pages verify, this was far from the old-time patient, slow development pace. It was a spectacular period of growth in which not one or two but literally hundreds of new laser systems were invented.

Despite this, some observers—even some experts—were pessimistic. Even with all the thousands of man-hours of research, they said, basically the laser was a laboratory tool as the 1960s drew to a close. This was mainly true, but the laser was already being put to use in small applications almost as soon as it was invented. Looking back in the history of technology, this was an amazing record compared to the lapse of from decades to hundreds of years from some major discoveries to their use in practical systems. The principles of electricity, for instance, were known for many tens of years before working electric motors were available.

But by the late 1960s only eight years after the first laser was operated, the evidence was on the side of those who believed the laser had moved from adolescence in. the first bloom of adulthood. The most important uses were still in the future, but lasers were doing important tasks in many sections of industry and in such vital fields as medicine and chemical analysis.

While each particular application didn't account for a great many laser purchases, taken together the total of actual uses was impressive. A list of 673 applications had been compiled by Dr. Richard G. Seed, president of Seed Electronics Corporation of New York. In addition, as he told a laser seminar in New York, he could show another list of 300 more possible laser tasks being studied by various research and development groups.

Professor Arthur Schawlow, who had joined Dr. Charles Townes in predicting the possibility of the laser in 1958, a decade later emphatically stated his views that the laser had come of age. In November 1968, Schawlow told an overflow audience at Stanford University (where he had become a member of the faculty) that the "incredible laser" is now "credible" and could no longer be called "a solution looking for a problem." In his talk, part of a special series on "Physics and Man," he said, "The laser is just getting out of the beginning airplane stage. We are getting past the laser [cynics], and needs are beginning to appear. Within the next couple of years, people who have the means will begin to come and ask for the laser to do their job, and at their price."

By the last statement, he underlined his feeling that good systems were already available to do many jobs. These were expensive, costing from a few thousand to many thousands of dollars. But the only reason they were so costly was their limited rate of production. The lasers

1968 were basically handmade, Schawlow pointed out. As soon as the demand for mass production came along, costs would come down sharply.

For some things, though, it may be hard to measure value in terms of price alone. At the time of Schawlow's talk, surgeons already were increasingly turning to lasers to score dramatic gains in treating some of man's ills. For a hospital, the price of $1000 or $2000 for a device that could be used to treat a great many patients did not seem excessive. By the end of the 1960s, eye surgeons were using lasers routinely for some things, such as welding torn, delicate eye tissues back in place or instantly and painlessly destroying damaging tumors on the retina.

As Schawlow stressed, doctors were carefully studying other possible uses for the laser on animals before extending the work to humans. This had been the approach followed in detached retina work before it was approved for conventional surgery. "It seems that some lasers might be useful for surgery on organs like the spleen, which have very large numbers of blood vessels. The laser will cauterize, or 'burn-heal,' as it cuts. For cancer, the results are entirely controversial. Some people have had good results, some have had very bad results." These results, of course, were made on test specimens, but the fact that some tests were successful indicates that lasers someday may be in the forefront of the war against one of mankind's most dreaded diseases.

Some of the semimedical uses of the laser have helped people feel happier and more self-confident without necessarily involving diseases. Thus the laser has given skin doctors a tool so precise that annoying blemishes or scars can often be removed simply and with no inconvenience.

One example given by Schawlow is the removal of tattoos. This use seems funny to many but, Schawlow points out, "I've met people who are terribly embarrassed by tattoos. This use is very important to them. And there is also the medical aspect that some tattoos seem to produce a precancerous condition."

It can be seen that the laser beam can be directed at the most sensitive parts of the human anatomy with complete safety. This may seem surprising, considering the tremendous energy found in a ray of coherent light. The temperature measured in a laser beam from a typical ruby laser, for instance, can be millions of times above that detected on the sun's surface. The brightness of the laser beam also can be far above that of the rays emitted by the sun. Why, then, the reader might ask, can this be directed at human tissue or the surface of all kinds of substances without causing wholesale destruction?

Part of the answer is the nature of coherence. The laser beam can be made so small in diameter that it affects only a very minute area of anything it touches. In addition, like any beam of light, it can be focused by a lens. Because of its properties, this focusing can be thousands of times more precise than an incoherent beam. Thus the searing energy of a laser beam can be concentrated in an extremely small area. For instance, the beam can remove just a few atoms of a surface and leave everything else in the material completely undisturbed.

In addition, the power output of the laser can be controlled so that only a small amount of energy is applied to a delicate target, such as human tissue, or a large amount when the equipment is intended for such things as drilling through metal or diamond.

Another thing that minimizes the problems of exposure to the laser is the effect of air on the beam. The atmosphere tends to diffuse—or spread out—the light beam. Thus the greatest part of the heat energy in the laser is dissipated over a relatively short distance just in burning a path through the air. This minimizes handling problems, though it is a very limiting factor on the use of the laser in earth-based communications systems.

The ease with which a laser beam can be focused over short distances, though, makes it a very promising device for many industrial processes. The laser's use in precisely aligning equipment or systems has been mentioned. Besides being used in factories to line up parts being assembled, it has been similarly applied in construction projects such as the new San Francisco Bay Area Rapid Transit System.

In the latter project, lasers were used to line up the drills occupied in boring the train tunnel under the bay from downtown San Francisco to Oakland. The approach saved both time and money for the project. The precise alignment achieved with the laser ensured that the drill did not have to be constantly reoriented so that it didn't start cutting away from the correct path. At the same time, keeping the drill properly adjusted minimized the chance of cutting away too much dirt and rock in some places, an action that would just be a waste of time and effort.

By the end of the 1960s, hundreds of companies across the United States had found important applications for lasers in assembling or shaping all kinds of materials.

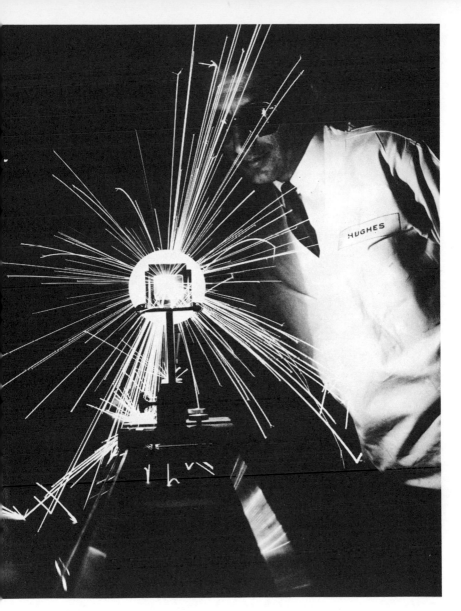

32. This looks like a fireworks display, but it's actually a picture of a ruby laser piercing a hole through a sheet of the extremely hard metal tantalum. Though tantalum has a boiling point of 10,000 degrees F., the laser drills the hole in less than 1/1000th of a second.

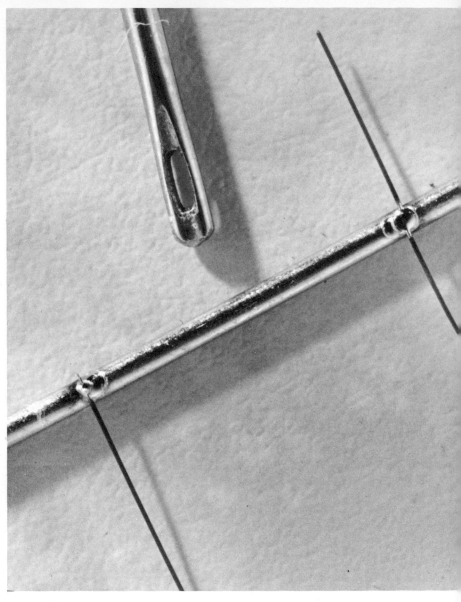

33. *Fantastic accuracy possible with a laser welder is indicated by this magnified picture of very fine wires (0.003-inch-diameter tungsten at top and 0.02-inch nickel at bottom) welded to a wire roughly the size of the needle shown at right. Welds such as this are performed routinely in assembly of microminiature electronic systems.*

Most of these operations would have been difficult or impossible to do any other way.

Some of the advantages of lasers for manufacturing are listed by G. E. Erb, product line manager for commercial industrial lasers at Hughes Aircraft Company:

"Nothing touches the weld; there is no physical contact of the laser device with the material to be welded, drilled, or machined. Therefore there is no danger of the pressure of the tool causing distortion, warping, or movement of the material being processed. For the same reason, there is no possibility of inducing outside electric or magnetic charges in the material." Such unwanted changes could so impair the properties of some delicate electronic parts or assemblies as to make them unusable. Because the laser tool doesn't cause such errors, it can weld, drill, or machine very delicate electronic components.

"One can process material in tight or otherwise inaccessible places. The light beam can remove material or make connections, for example, deep inside long narrow holes. Using mirrors to direct the beam at special angles, the laser can do work in hard-to-reach sections of complicated assemblies."

The revolutionary laser also plays a vital role in another technological breakthrough of recent years, microelectronics. Microelectronics refers to the shrinking of electronic devices to an extreme degree. With today's microelectronic technology, for instance, it is literally possible to build a complete radio circuit in an area little larger than the head of a pin. A typical device in the new microelectronics technology is a circuit board about the size of a dime containing 20,000 transistors.

To connect such microscopic devices to other devices

or to perform machining or drilling steps can be a problem unless very accurate tools are available. As Erb stresses, the laser can do such minute tasks with relative ease. "We can weld wires much thinner than a human hair to thin film electronic layers thousandths of an inch thick. In drilling or machining operations, we can remove extremely small portions of metal so fast there is no time for heat distortion of very sensitive materials. Typically, the strongest metal can be machined precisely where desired in two milliseconds."

Laser welders also can weld materials that could not be

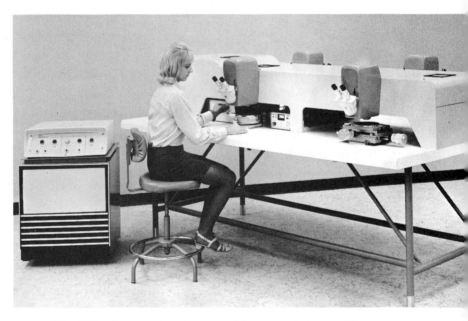

34. This four-station laser welder was being sold to electronic manufacturing companies by Hughes Aircraft Company in the early 1970s. The four stations operate on the beam from a single neodymium-YAG laser which is split by a mirror system and distributed to the stations.

joined by regular methods. For instance, glass could be welded to steel, a ceramic to a plastic material, or two normally unweldable metals to each other. Some of these combinations can be joined by another new electromagnetic tool, the electron beam welder, which shoots a stream of high-speed electrons at the weld joint. However, the electron beam is much more easily scattered and reduced in power by the air than the concentrated laser beam. As a result, electron beam welding must be done in a vacuum chamber. On the other hand, the laser has few problems with the atmospheric envelope over short distances and so can be used in any normal factory environment.

One of the features of a laser beam is that it can pass through transparent or semi-transparent materials without cutting or damaging them, provided the proper focusing is done. Thus it is possible to use optical lenses to focus the beam so it will weld, drill, or machine materials through a window or other transparent material. As Erb points out, "We have welded delicate wires and parts together through the Scotch tape holding them in place."

Some of the uses of the laser in commerce and industry might verge on the comic to an outsider, but to the user, the only reason it would bring a smile is because of the savings in time and energy the laser brings. An example is the growing use of coherent light in the cattle industry. There probably will be little public interest in a cowboy song that might have lyrics such as "I'm an old cowhand/with my laser brand," and it's highly unlikely we'll see any western movies with laser-totin' heroes and villains. To cattle raisers, though, the new device is a welcome development, promising major savings

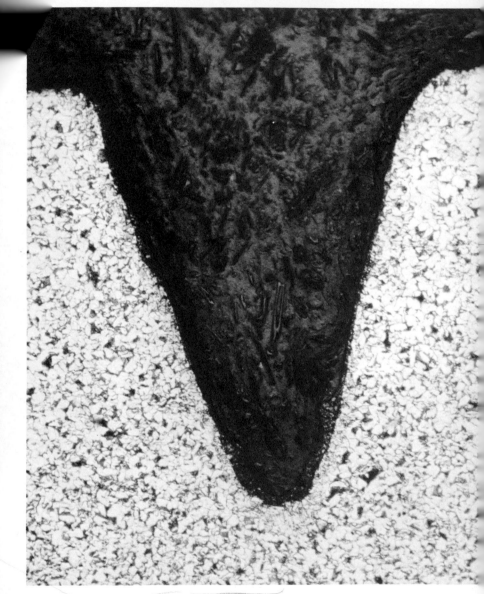

35. This photomicrograph (100 times actual size) shows a cross section of a hole generated in a block of mild steel by a burst from a production-type laser.

at a time when inflation continues to hit hard at rancher as well as farmers.

The laser system was developed by the Veterinary Research Institute, Dallas, Texas, to streamline the processing of cattle delivered by ranchers to feed lot operators. The main goal was to save the operators money, but the technique also proves much more humane for the animals.

The time-honored way of handling steers at the feed lot has been to run the animal into a chute with movable sides. These sides clamp the steer in place for a series of usually painful operations: the animal is branded with a hot iron, its horns are cut off, and other surgical steps are taken. All of these things normally are so harrowing to the steer he loses his appetite for some days afterward. As a result, the animal loses twenty-five to fifty pounds of weight the feed lot operator can never restore.

Hot iron branding alone is estimated to cause a yearly loss of $50 million by the Tanners Hide Bureau. The reason is that the heat from the brand can spread to a large area of the hide, making it impossible to use it for good leather items.

VRI tests showed that a carbon dioxide laser could do the entire job of branding, dehorning, and surgically preparing the animal for feed lot use in a matter of seconds. (Laser branding is done by placing a stencil over the hide and lasing the exposed area.) The cost of branding alone is cut from twenty-five to forty cents a hide to only twelve to fifteen cents. The rapid action of the laser and the fact that its effect is so localized make it possible to do all these operations to the steer without causing any pain at all. The fact that the beam cauterizes

...ne tissue as it works also eliminates the infections that can occur with conventional methods. Finally, these advantages ensure that the steer will eat normally right away and there is no more weight loss. The value of this technique to the cattle industry is estimated at several hundred million dollars a year, which hopefully will also be reflected in lower prices for the meat the housewife places on the table.

The energy present in a laser beam is demonstrated by its ability to cut through the hardest, toughest materials. Thus lasers have been used to cut holes thousandths of an inch in diameter through the hardest material known to man, the diamond. Properly focused, a laser beam can also cut through many layers of materials at one time, leading to great promise for many sheet-metal applications.

One such application is the use of a carbon dioxide laser to make steel dies for production of cardboard cartons. The laser can make more of these dies at one time than a conventional flame-cutting die machine and with much sharper die cutting edges. In an automated system designed for the packaging system by Coherent Radiation Company, Palo Alto, California, a computer is used to solve the equations giving the desired dimensions of the carton die. Signals from the computer then focus the laser beam and move the carriage holding the laser along the desired paths needed to cut the metal material to shape.

While laser tools can work very well in air, they are even better in vacuum surroundings. In fact, without interference from the gases that make up the atmosphere, a laser beam can travel millions of miles with only slight spreading or loss of energy, which makes coherent light so attractive for space communications. (See Chapter V.)

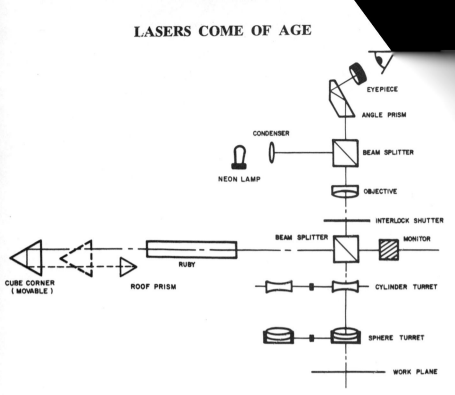

36. Main parts of a laser welder are indicated in this diagram. Neon lamp is used to illuminate the workpiece for the welder operator. Movable optics at left are used to change the properties of the beam from a ruby laser which then focused by the machine turret optics on the part being welded. (Weld area is referred to as "work plane.")

Thus laser welders promise to play a major role in the construction of massive orbiting space facilities. Tests run by the Materials Joining Techniques Division of Battelle Memorial Institute, Columbus, Ohio, show that excellent laser-made spot welds of such metals as aluminum and titanium can be made under vacuum conditions.

Because a laser beam is affected by the atmosphere, it can also be used to find out things about this vitally

37. This compact laser trimmer, used to trim solid-state electronic parts to accuracies of under 0.1 per cent, was finding a good market in industry in the early 1970s at a price of $14,275 per instrument.

important "orange peel" covering of earth. A laser beam has difficulty in penetrating clouds, dense fogs, etc., but this can be used by meteorologists to locate and map such features of earth's atmosphere. The rate of absorption of energy from a light beam and the reflections sent back to earth from solid particles in the air can be used to determine the particles of matter present at various altitudes.

As a result, an instrument called the lidar (Light tection and Ranging) has been invented for meteorologie work. The original lidar was built in 1964 by a team of scientists and engineers at Stanford Research Institute. They mounted a laser on a gun mount along with

38. *Pulsed ruby laser is shown vaporizing a 0.02-inch-diameter crater into the surface of a stainless steel part at a temperature of 4800 degrees F.*

...otocell detector. The mount could be moved to point
...e laser skyward in any desired direction. The laser
could then be turned on and reflections from the beam
picked up by the photocell. By sending a series of laser
pulses to the area under study while the mount slowly
performed a scanning pattern, it was possible to make
charts of the reflections indicating the presence of special
features.

On the very first night the lidar was operated, experimenters gained new and sometimes unexpected information about the atmosphere. Myron Ligda, the head of the
Stanford Research Institute Aerophysics Laboratory, found
he could detect things in the atmosphere previously ob-
servable with difficulty or not at all. Among the new
data were reflections from the upper atmosphere thirty
miles above the earth's surface. These indicated the presence of some light reflecting layers that meteorologists
had not been aware of before.

Since then, lidars have been built that have provided
much new insight into the workings of the air masses.
Lidars can measure cloud heights far above the altitudes
previously detectable from earth. They can also be used
to measure the speed of approaching fogs, map the presence of meteoritic dust particles in the air, and, through
the use of special optical filters placed in front of the
laser lens, indicate whether a cloud is growing in size or
dying out. Lidars also can detect unusual air patterns
invisible to other optical systems. In particular, they
are mapping the occurrence of clear air turbulence (CAT)
—a situation in which air currents of stormlike intensity
develop even though the region seems completely calm,
clear, and peaceful to the unaided eye. It is hoped that

these studies will help predict the presence of CA so eliminate a major danger to air travel.

Possibly the most important use of this kind of optic radar system is in the fight against pollution. One of the problems facing scientists is the need to know what kind of pollutants are in the atmosphere and how they are distributed. Not only is it vital to know these patterns at the time they are being measured, but also to know how they compare to the state of the atmosphere in the past. Just like weather prediction, it's important for meteorologists and anti-pollution experts to detect trends indicating the increase or decrease of contaminants throughout the air. Lidar supplied one of the first ground-based instruments able to provide this kind of information.

An area of technology in which laser applications received intensive study starting in the late 1960s is that of computers. Every company in the massive data-processing field—one that such experts as Robert Muchmore of TRW Systems predicts will surpass the automobile industry as the most important in the U.S. economy by the 1980s—has a program dealing with optical computer systems. The reason is the great improvement in computer performance promised by the optical approach. Writing in *Industrial Research** magazine, Kendall Preston, Jr., member of the senior research staff for Perkin-Elmer Corporation, pointed out, "Optical computers literally are as fast as the speed of light because the input is processed almost instantaneously by a beam of light. By comparison, electronic computers are slow—it takes a finite length of time for the signal to be processed by the computer circuits."

*June 1969, p. 58.

enious techniques have been devised to apply laser .t to high-speed computers. Usually these methods make se of special production methods developed in microelectronics technology.

An example of this are the new kinds of devices called Membrane Light Modulators, or MLMs. The MLM makes use of a series of tiny, deflectable, mirrorlike parts to convert commands or information from an operator into light signals that will run the optical computer. The MLMs are important because they can put data into an optical computer at a speed that matches that possible for the computer itself. Conventional electronic parts, such as transistors and diodes, cannot do this. The optical input can provide such improvement in input rates that even where standard electronic technology is desirable for the computer, laser-operated inputs may be used.

Most MLM devices to date have been made by carefully depositing layers of special materials on a high strength glass base. This is done by covering the surface of the glass with extremely accurate masks. These masks block off all of the glass except for a series of tiny openings just the right size for circular membrane elements. The masked glass is placed in a vacuum chamber and the surface openings are exposed to successive flows of vaporized materials. At first, for instance, a chromium vapor is directed through the chamber, depositing a thin layer of this metal directly on the open circles of glass showing through the mask. In order, several more very thin layers are deposited on top of the chromium: first a layer of gold, then a porous layer of silicon dioxide, then a thin plastic membrane. Finally, an extremely thin metal film is deposited on the membrane; this film is made of a metal that will present a shiny, mirrorlike s

Both the gold layer and the metalized films are g conductors of electric current and both are connected electric terminals. When the operator wants to transmit information to the computer, he operates controls that send signals to the appropriate gold electrodes. Those electrodes receiving the flow of electricity set up an electrostatic force field with the metalized layer. This field passes through the porous layer and the membrane. When the voltage reaches a certain level, the field becomes strong enough to deflect the membrane.

The glass plate with its surface of small membranes is positioned at roughly a forty-five-degree angle to a beam of light from a laser. The metalized surfaces each can reflect some of the laser light into the optics of the computer. When any of the membranes are deflected, the light reflected into the computer is changed in phase from that of the undeflected surfaces. The computer optics are designed to detect these changes and to make the necessary calculations based on the light patterns.

In digital computers, lasers promise important gains in the all-important memory systems. These memories store information that can later be retrieved by the computer electronics and used to solve particular problems. In effect, the computer memory is an electronic reference library. Obviously, the more bits of data that can be stored in the memory, the greater the number of calculations the system can perform. Studies of coherent light properties show that a major increase in storage capacity can be gained. The beam from an argon ion laser, as Richard N. Einhorn of Electronic Design points out, can be focused to a spot less than a micron in diameter be-

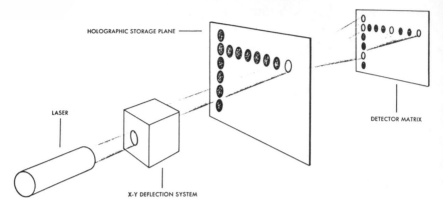

HOLOGRAPHIC STORAGE PLANE

LASER

DETECTOR MATRIX

X-Y DEFLECTION SYSTEM

39. Diagram of an optical memory using a holographic plate to store information. Information is recovered when the beam from a laser is directed to the proper holographic dot by the x-7 deflector unit. The detector matrix in the background picks up the light signals from the hologram and converts them to electrical signals for use in the computer.

cause of the short optical wavelength. "Theoretically," he notes, "storage densities could approach a billion bits per square centimeter." By comparison, the highest density achieved in the most advanced conventional computers of the 1960s was several hundred thousand bits per square centimeter.

The general method used in laser memories is to direct a very small diameter laser beam to precise spots on a special recording material. There are a number of different ways of controlling the direction of the beam. One method that provides excellent control is called a scanlaser. The scanlaser has electronic circuitry that directs a stream of electrons at the laser crystal. These electrons suppress all the modes of the laser light coming out of the crystal except for the one that will provide a beam in e. the right place.

The recording material can take a number of forms including photographic films, special light-sensitive solid materials or magnetic material. The information is stored by using the laser beam to change the properties of the recording material in exactly the correct locations. (The recording material might be thought of as a very large grid of cross-reference dots. Each of these tiny dots has an exact address. For instance, it might be on line number 1000 in the X direction and line 2341 in the Y direction. The laser beam changes the properties of a series of dots that stands for the stored data, and the system has circuitry to keep track of the locations for future use.)

As an example of the way information is "written" in a magnetic type memory, we might consider the system developed by the Honeywell Research Center, Hopkins, Minnesota. In this case, the storage material was a thin film of manganese bismuth. The power of the laser beam is raised until it applies just enough heat to change the magnetic properties of tiny sections of the manganese bismuth, but not enough to damage the material. As the spot cools, a magnetic field can be applied to change the direction of the magnetization of the spot. The spot, in effect, is a tiny magnet, and the direction in which it points describes the bit of information stored in the memory. (This might be compared to a compass needle, though the analogy is only broadly true. The needle tells us whether the direction we want to go is north, north-north-west, etc.)

Tests indicated this system could store thirty times as much data for a given memory area as a conventional

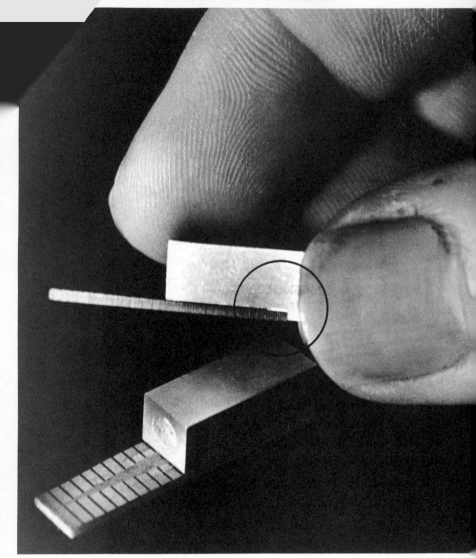

40. & 41. The tiny size laser for computer memories made possible by using special solid-state materials is demonstrated by this
IBM photograph. The diagram indicates the way twenty gallium
arsenide lasers are installed in the small memory unit shown in the
picture.

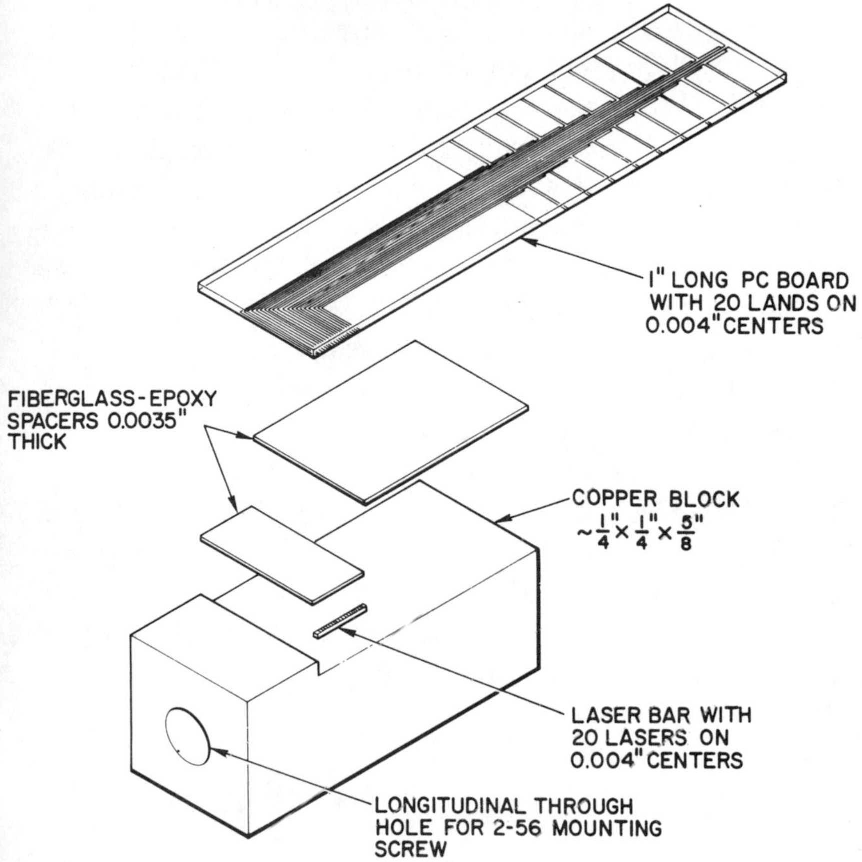

1" LONG PC BOARD
WITH 20 LANDS ON
0.004" CENTERS

FIBERGLASS-EPOXY
SPACERS 0.0035"
THICK

COPPER BLOCK
$\sim \frac{1}{4}" \times \frac{1}{4}" \times \frac{5}{8}"$

LASER BAR WITH
20 LASERS ON
0.004" CENTERS

LONGITUDINAL THROUGH
HOLE FOR 2-56 MOUNTING
SCREW

memory, and this information could be retrieved when needed a hundred times as fast as in previous systems.

Not only can such a system store a great deal of information in a small area, it can also be designed to fit into a very small package with the laser source included. This is done by using semiconductors as the source of the coherent light. In 1970, for example, IBM demonstrated laser "mini-arrays" made up of not one but many lasers that fit easily in the palm of the hand. By

, such materials as gallium arsenide, it was noted in apter III, a laser can be made smaller than a grain of sand. With this approach, IBM produced compact computer memories using rows of miniature lasers. A typical design had twenty gallium arsenide bars, each of which contained twenty lasers having the hard-to-visualize dimensions of 0.0008 inch long by 0.0005 inch wide. As in the Honeywell system, the IBM mini-array "writes" by heating tiny spots on magnetically affected material. In the IBM system, though, a rare earth film, europium oxide, is the storage medium.

To these few examples of laser applications, many more could be added affecting almost every phase of business and industry. And we have not yet discussed what promises to be one of the most dramatic of all areas, the use of lasers in communications. Truly, as the 1970s began, the laser had come of age.

CHAPTER V

NEW COMMUNICATIONS REVOLUTION

At the start of the 1970s, thousands of lasers were in use, either in laboratories or for some of the applications mentioned earlier. Impressive as this may seem, all these efforts taken together only added up to yearly sales of $90 to $100 million. This figure falls far short of the billion-dollar potential forecast for the "light fantastic." In fact, it was only about 10 per cent of the sales volume of long-playing records in 1970.

Laser experts were not daunted, because they were sure that programs already in advanced development would eventually make their technology one of the most important in the world's economy. In particular, they pointed to the field of communications as the one that would make the laser a household word.

As Dr. Maiman stressed in 1970, there really was no immediate need for using lasers for mass communications. The phone systems of the United States, for instance, had more than enough capacity to handle the expected volume of phone messages for at least the first part of the 1970s. Not only that, he noted, it would be a long time before the laser phone system would be available that could handle coast-to-coast messages for a dollar a call.

though, Maiman as well as the officials of major munications systems knew there would be a need for more capacity than conventional phone lines could handle. The most promising answer was in coherent light technology. As Parker Sullivan, president of General Telephone Company of California, affirmed, "The laser is the most important single scientific project now under development in the field of communications."

As one General Telephone executive put it, "The message-carrying potential of light is enormous. For example,

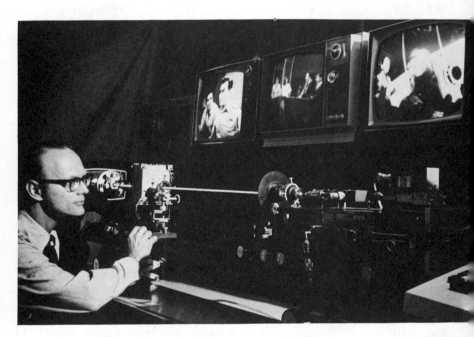

42. *Dr. Robert Ohlmann of Lockheed Missiles & Space Company operates a green laser beam system that is carrying signals from all of the commercial TV channels in the San Francisco region. Some of this information is being used to transmit the three different programs shown on the TV sets at the top of the picture.*

every single telephone call, radio and television pro.. and every other kind of communication taking place any time in the world could be transmitted over a singr. laser. An estimated 10 trillion separate messages could be transmitted at the same time. And since a laser beam is only about a millimeter in diameter and can be transmitted in any direction, a large number of beams could be used simultaneously on the same frequency.

"Then too, laser light waves are similar to those produced by a radio transmitter, but at a vastly higher frequency. And the higher the basic frequency, the greater the amount of information that can be transmitted."

The fact that all kinds of information could be communicated from one system to another had been demonstrated many times by the late 1960s. By 1967, for instance, scientists at Bell Laboratories had an experimental system working in their laboratory that could transmit two TV programs and thirty-six voice channels on a helium-neon laser beam. Operating over short distances, the quality shown on the TV screen was as good as that obtainable with conventional TV circuits.

In 1969, experimenters at Case Western Reserve University, Cleveland, Ohio, successfully linked two computer centers 300 meters apart using a laser system. Data from one center were fed into an electronic coder in the form of punched cards. The holes in the cards were used to generate electronic signals that impressed desired radiation patterns on the beam from a helium-neon laser. The light beam then traveled through the air to a detector at the other center that converted the light beam data into electronic signals that operated a computer.

W. Bruce Johnson, head of the university's Electrical

...ces and Applied Science Division, told *Industrial Re-search* magazine, "This is the first operational data link in the nation which uses a laser to send information long distances from one computer to another." He predicted that in a few years' time the program would permit interconnecting many information centers by lasers over distances of up to eight kilometers.

In the early 1970s, a number of facilities were using laser links of this kind over short distances. However, all of these uses were for specialized programs that did not require operation 100 per cent of the time. The stumbling block to mass operations was the effect of many outside events on transmission of laser beams through the air. A great many things can block passage of a coherent beam. Any solid object can pose a problem: if someone raised a large mirror in the path of a laser beam, the beam would be reflected off in some other direction. As a Bell Laboratories scientist told one reporter, "We couldn't plan a major telephone system in which the laser beam would be sent through the atmosphere. One bird flying through the beam could interrupt 10 million calls."

Not only can birds, low-flying planes, and other moving objects interfere, so can atmospheric disturbances. Clouds, rain, snow all can distort or stop light rays sent from most laser systems. The problem could be minimized in some cases by increasing the power of the beam so it could burn its way through atmospheric interference, but this could pose health problems to life forms getting in the way of the beam. These problems would not be lethal, but the beam would probably have to be strong enough

to threaten eye damage to a person looking directly
the incoming ray.

(The fact that laser beams can be made powerfu
enough to severely injure or even kill someone caused
many writers to talk of the laser as providing the death
ray that has long been a favorite theory of science fiction.
However, few laser experts will agree that a laser death
ray will ever be practical. They stress that by the time
you do all that is necessary to build a laser weapon
you find it really isn't as good as the conventional arsenal
that man has already developed for the unhappy art of
war.

(As Dr. Maiman points out, "Most uses, as now, will
be fairly mundane. I don't expect to see such wild ideas
as a death ray come to pass. In fact, such predictions
are misleading because they imply this is an application,
but it's rather unlikely it will ever become a reality. The
laser is not all that tactical. In a weapon, you're trying
to deliver energy from one place to another and bullets
have tremendous energy storage per unit volume. With a
laser, to get comparable energy from one place to another
requires huge power supplies, the problem of severe over-
heating, etc. As one scientist said, 'If the target is close
enough to do serious damage with lasers, by then you
could hit him over the head with a hammer.'")

However, there are many safe and valuable laser communications applications that will use transmission through
the air. A computer network is one of these. Dr. George
Smith of Hughes Research Laboratories gave some of the
advantages. "The limitations of phone line terminals are
obvious to companies spread out in many locations in one
region. For instance, our research laboratories are about

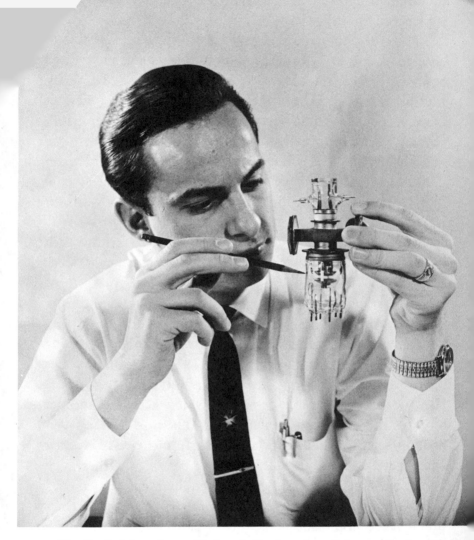

43. *Technician from National Engineering Science Company, Pasadena, California, holds a special demodulator tube for an experimental laser communications system. The tube converts signals carried by a laser beam back into electrical current to produce audible or visible signals.*

twenty miles from our main engineering building. can't afford a big computer at the laboratory, but engineering division can. We have a phone line we ca use to send problems by underground cable to the central computer, but this line has a limited capacity for electrical signals.

"The more complicated the problem our scientists want to solve, the more electronic signals are needed. For some problems, the phone line doesn't have enough capacity. Then we have to make up a program on punched cards, send it by messenger to the central computer, and wait until he brings back the answer. So for a few minutes' computer time, a scientist or engineer may have to sit around a whole day for results."

The tremendous capacity of a laser beam would solve such a dilemma. Even though weather would interfere on occasion, Smith noted it would be only a minor hindrance. "Just as planes may be grounded during severe weather disturbances, a large company or organization can put up with the fact that occasionally the laser system might be out of operation."

Smith's optimistic statement was based on the fact that Hughes Research Laboratories had completed preliminary tests by the late 1960s, indicating that good short-range laser communications were possible. In particular, the Hughes team proved out the theory of a "window" for certain laser frequencies in the atmosphere.

Basically, the atmosphere fights the transmission of light beams in almost all frequencies in or near the visible range. Physicists, though, ran calculations and tests indicating there were certain frequencies at which radiation is only slightly distorted by the air. These frequencies, ed to as a "window in the atmosphere," are not ne visible spectrum but in the infrared between values eight and thirteen microns. Laser experimenters were particularly excited by this because the midpoint of this range—about 10.6 microns—is the frequency of the output of the CO_2 laser. This laser, as we have noted in previous pages, is one of the most powerful and efficient coherent light systems.

In 1968, a Hughes engineering team led by Frank E. Goodwin designed a carbon dioxide system using two CO_2 lasers, one in the research laboratory in Malibu, California, and the other at a Hughes facility in Baldwin Hills. Special solid-state crystals were used to code and later detect signals on the laser beam. On the transmitter side, the coding was done by a carefully prepared gallium arsenide crystal, a material that can work as a laser in other devices. The detector was made of germanium, a familiar transistor material. One interesting feature was the use of reflecting telescopes to send and receive the beam. This was necessary because, while the atmosphere has a window at 10.6 microns, optical glass does not. Thus lenses can't be used to process the carbon dioxide signals; reflecting mirrors are required instead.

When the system began operating, the sky was bright and clear and reception was excellent. The question remained, how would things go when the dense, ground-hugging fogs rolled in from the ocean, or the occasional rainstorms of the Southern California winter arose? A few weeks after the test began, there were several days of light fog. Though there was some interference, the signals still got through. The tests continued for four months mostly with excellent conditions, but sometimes with fogs

EOS LASER BEACON SYSTEM

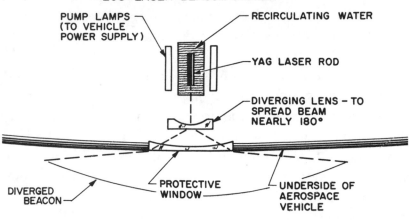

PUMP LAMPS
(TO VEHICLE
POWER SUPPLY)

RECIRCULATING WATER

YAG LASER ROD

DIVERGING LENS – TO
SPREAD BEAM
NEARLY 180°

DIVERGED
BEACON

PROTECTIVE
WINDOW

UNDERSIDE OF
AEROSPACE
VEHICLE

TRACKING MODE

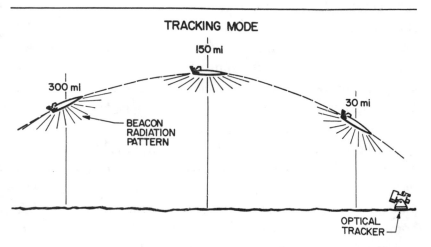

150 mi

300 mi

30 mi

BEACON
RADIATION
PATTERN

OPTICAL
TRACKER

44. Important use of the laser is in providing position information of vehicles. Example is indicated in these diagrams of a laser beacon developed by Electro-Optical Systems Division of Xerox. The beam from the YAG laser passes through the special optical systems in the bottom of the craft, then proceeds down through the atmosphere until detected by an optical tracker.

avy engineers could barely see across the street. noise content of the signals rose noticeably during ad weather, but usually not enough to prevent the detecting electronics from deciphering the messages. At the end of the program, Goodwin could report "weather conditions were seldom bad enough to prevent operation."

The equipment was still too expensive for general use in industry, but the window proposal was no longer just a theory. Other groups began considering it for deep space laser systems able to transmit signals to and from earth for distances as great as 50 million miles. These scientists reasoned that if the window was exploited to send signals directly up (or down) through the atmosphere, the distance between the thin upper layers of air and the earth's surface is hardly much greater than that involved in such point-to-point programs as Hughes'. Once away from the atmosphere, the laser beam could travel almost indefinitely in the void of space without much further degradation.

By the end of the 1960s, the National Aeronautics and Space Administration was receiving promising reports on carbon dioxide communications systems from several companies. Among those developing equipment under NASA contracts were Honeywell Systems and Research Center; Sylvania Electric Division of General Telephone & Electronics Corp.; and Airborne Instruments Laboratory.

The Honeywell work was aimed at providing a laser transmitter for deep space communications similar to the CO_2 network demonstrated by Hughes. The main difference was that the carbon dioxide in the Honeywell laser flowed continuously through the optical cavity, whereas the Hughes laser sealed a certain amount of the gas inside. Based on early tests of the system, Honeywell scientist Dr. Hans W. Mocker estimated that a highly sensitive, very long-range space network could result. His studies indicated the earth-based laser receiver could pick up a signal as weak as one 10-trillionth of a watt from a spacecraft 50 million miles away. This distance is roughly that from the vicinity of Mars to our planet.

Once beyond earth's atmosphere, of course, there is no need for an atmospheric window. In space, therefore, any kind of a laser can be used to send signals for considerable distances. As a result, NASA has supported studies of many different kinds of laser communications systems for deep space transmission. Particular attention has been given to sun-pumped designs—devices that collect light directly from the sun's rays to provide the energy needed to excite laser materials to the desired levels for lasing.

As early as 1964, a relatively simple sun-pumped system was demonstrated by Electro-Optical Systems, Inc., of Pasadena, California. The device used a highly polished, thirty-inch-diameter parabolic reflector to concentrate solar energy. This energy was fed to a YAG (Yttrium Aluminum Garnet) laser rod positioned in the center of the reflector inside a water-filled glass flask. The water flask was designed to work as a liquid lens to refract solar energy over the entire two-inch length of the YAG rod. At the same time, the water provided cooling for the laser. The output from the laser, directed out from the underside of the reflector-YAG assembly, could then be coded with signal patterns before beginning its long journey through space to the receiving system.

NASA supported some work in crystal devices, but, by

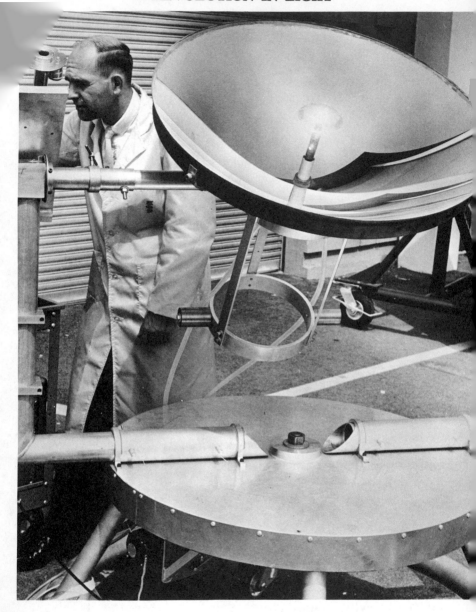

45. & 46. *A sun pumped laser may be used in future space vehicles. One such laser, developed by Electro-Optical Systems,*

the end of the decade, agency scientists leaned toward sun-pumped semiconductor injection lasers. The semiconductor approach offered the combination of extremely shockproof, rugged devices that also could be made so small as to save a great deal of spacecraft weight. The electrical energy needed to run an injection laser can be

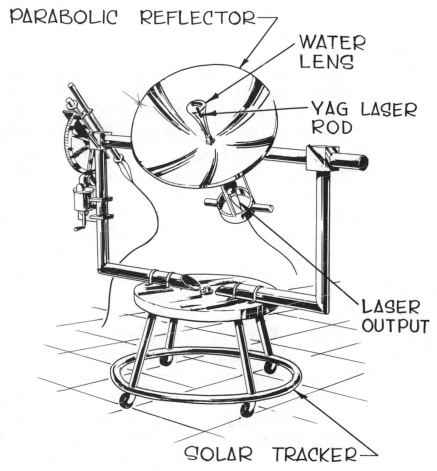

PARABOLIC REFLECTOR

WATER LENS

YAG LASER ROD

LASER OUTPUT

SOLAR TRACKER

uses a highly polished reflector to concentrate sun's rays on a laser rod installed in a water lens.

gained by focusing the sun's rays from a parabolic mirror on an array of solar cells, devices that convert solar energy directly into a flow of electricity. By the end of the 1960s, several systems were built or designed for NASA. One of these, built by RCA for the Manned Space-craft Center, was used to transmit experimental television pictures.

A possible space transmission system of the future might use several different laser designs. For example, a laser operating at frequencies outside those of earth's laser transmission window could send signals between space vehicles and an orbiting satellite. The satellite could then reprocess the signals so that a CO_2 device could retrans-mit them through the atmosphere to earth. The combined efficiency of two or more varied systems might prove greater than using a single laser for the complete opera-tion.

At the time Apollo 11 began its historic mission to the moon, there were still many engineering problems remaining to be solved before practical space laser trans-mitters would be available. The Apollo astronauts com-municated with earth by conventional radio and TV circuitry. However, their mission did accomplish the po-tential of coherent light. One of the odd-looking instru-ments they carried onto the bleak, dusty surface of the moon, in full view of hundreds of millions on earth, was a special reflector.

This highly polished unit was part of an important laser ranging experiment. Soon after Neil Armstrong and Edward Aldrin stepped aboard their craft and blasted off on the first leg of their voyage home, laser beams from Arizona streaked through cislunar space toward the reflector. These beams came from a laser installed on a sixty-inch telescope by astronomers and engineers from Hughes Aircraft Company.

The coherent light went into space in a series of short bursts, each of which arrived at the moon's surface a few seconds after the one before. In the vicinity of the moon, these concentrations of light energy took the shape of "Giant pancakes," as one expert described them, roughly 2½ miles wide by 10 feet thick. These dimensions seem large, but they actually are amazingly small, considering the tremendous distance covered.

It took some time for the scientists to zero in on the reflector, which apparently was knocked out of position by the spacecraft blast-off. However, in a few cases, some of the light from the pancakes was returned to earth. There an atomic clock timing device measured the light's round trip travel time to compute the distance from earth to moon to the unprecedented accuracy of ±1.5 meters.

Ranging experiments like these promised to be the forerunner of systems for pinpoint navigation and control of space vehicles of the future. Just as lasers are widely used on earth to line up tools and equipment to razor-thin accuracies, they will be similarly used to mate parts of future space stations or to assemble space trains to ferry astronauts and supplies to far-off sections of the solar system.

However, space spectaculars don't do too much to solve the problems of engineers trying to develop long distance phone, TV, or radio networks. The many interferences of the atmosphere make it necessary to find some way of beaming these kinds of laser beams under controlled conditions. The generally accepted answer is to install pipes

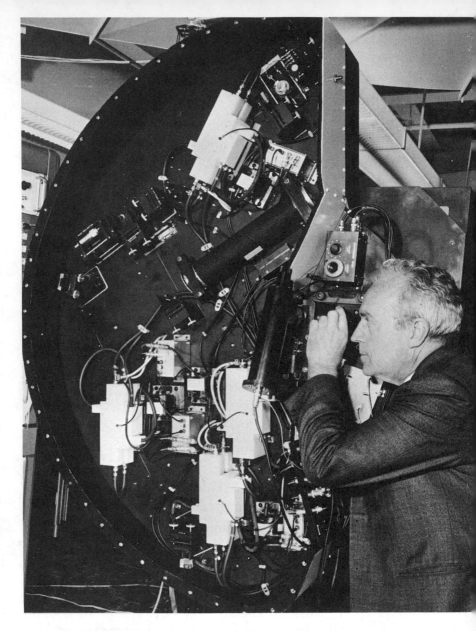

47. & 48. *This complicated-looking apparatus is the laser range finder used in Apollo 11 tests to accurately measure earth-moon distances. Dr. Renne S. Julian, Hughes Aircraft senior scientist, is shown sighting through the alignment device that aims the laser*

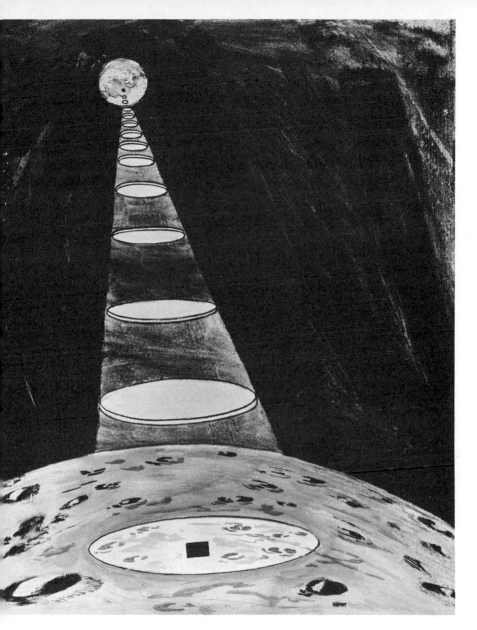

pulse at the desired location on the moon's surface. The artist's sketch shows how these pulses end up in "pancakes" of light 2½ miles wide by 10 feet thick that set up reflections from moon-based mirrors.

in the ground and send the laser beam from one place to another through these containers. However, this seeming solution raises a number of new problems.

For one thing, the laser pipe can't just be laid down with relatively little lining up, as is the case with phone cables. Phone cables can bend and the signals will still travel through them with no loss of power or information. A coherent light beam, on the other hand, will normally travel in a straight line unless some outside force is brought to bear on it to change its direction. Therefore, if the pipe containing it should bend, some or all of the beam may be absorbed or reflected backward by the pipe's inner surfaces. Even if the pipe could be placed down on what appeared to be a perfectly flat stretch of the earth's surface, problems would arise from the earth's curvature. Engineers point out that over a distance of 350 miles, the variation of a trace on earth's surface from a straight line may be as much as fifteen or sixteen miles.

Solving the problem of sending light hundreds or thousands of miles through pipes (or special variations known as waveguides) has occupied center stage for laser communications scientists. At the start of the 1970s, most of the equipment needed to put information into laser beams and send them out and to receive the beams and extract the data was more or less in hand. However, until low-cost ways were found to get the coherent light efficiently across long distances, mass laser communications could only be a dream.

For a while, most of the research was based on using lenses to focus the beam at intervals and steer it over curved surfaces or around corners. Difficulties in placing these lenses cropped up, though. Dr. Rudolph Kompfner of Bell Telephone Laboratories wrote in *Science* magazine, "If the distance between lenses is short, the beam will be kept close to the central axis and little of it will be lost by diffraction spreading. But the loss due to the lenses will be high. If the lenses are few and far between, there will be little loss from the lenses, but much from diffraction."

The U. S. Army Electronics Command came up with an alternate approach. Their engineers suggested using small sampling lenses along the edges of the beam located at intervals between relatively widely spaced focusing lenses. If the light beam was off center, more light would pass through the sampling lens, activating an electronic signal in wires connecting the lenses to the preceding focusing lens. These signals would cause a small motor at the focusing lens to reposition the lens just the right amount to recenter the beam. A major objection to this was expense. Building lenses into the pipe system already made installation of such networks costly; adding a repositioning system just increased the economic problems.

Toward the end of the 1960s, Bell scientists thought of a new technique that promised to show the way to a practical system. They proposed a system known as a gas lens. The coherent beam would be centered in pipes filled with flowing gas.

Because of friction effects along the walls of a pipe, a gas will slow down at the edges, but make up for this by moving faster at the center of the container. This phenomenon affects the temperature of the gas; the faster the flow, the cooler the gas, and vice versa. Most important of all, the cooler a gas, the denser it becomes. This density effect makes the gas a naturally converging

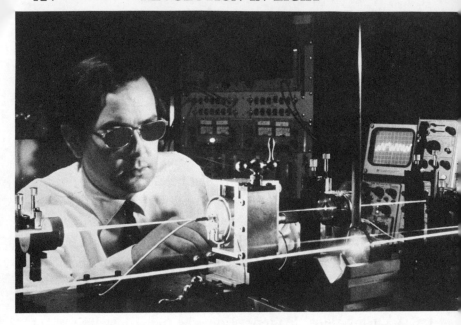

49. With multiplying communications needs, laser beams may be the only practical method of keeping up with the demand because of their tremendous information-carrying capacity. Example of this potential is the special input device being adjusted at Bell Telephone Laboratories by physicist Gerard White. This device can impress a billion pieces of information each second onto a single laser beam.

lens, pushing the beam of light always toward the center of the pipe.

Not only would the gas lens keep the beam centered, Bell Telephone scientists noted, it would also minimize losses due to reflections. The reason is that gas doesn't have the refracting surfaces of a lens or exposed pipe walls, and thus it causes few losses due to scattering of portions of the light beam.

Despite the potential of the gas lens, there were still

plenty of obstacles in the way of a successful system by the early 1970s. The pipes to hold the gas and light beam had to be aligned almost as precisely as for other transmission methods, and very accurate gas supply systems were required to provide just the right flow conditions. The problem facing scientists and engineers at this point was to come up with ways of minimizing the costs of assembling such a network so that it would make economic sense to put it into operation.

Whether the gas lens worked out or not, most laser experts believed a method would be worked out so the coherent beam could meet the needs of an expected five- or tenfold increase in phone calls by 1990. By that time, forecasters could see such new services as 55 million videophone calls a year going cross country in addition to radio, TV, and all the other operations already using phone lines today.

Long before then, lasers were destined to play an important role in home communications systems. In 1969, RCA Corporation announced development was underway on a revolutionary low-cost home color television player built around lasers and holography. Company officials predicted that when the system, called SelectaVision, moved off the production line in 1973 or '74, it would be the first consumer product to employ lasers.

RCA President Robert Sarnoff emphasized his belief that SelectaVision "should do for the visual arts what the phonograph record has done for its aural counterpart in providing the consumer access to a wide selection of entertainment and sports programs tailored to an unlimited variety of individual tastes."

Though other companies quickly announced more con-

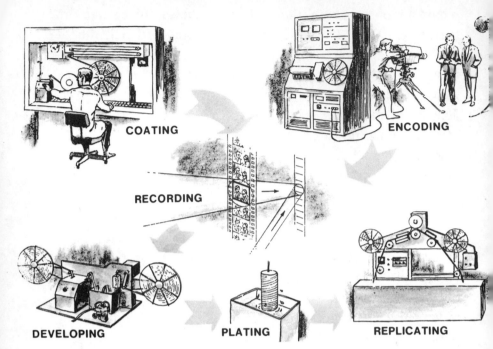

COATING

ENCODING

RECORDING

DEVELOPING

PLATING

REPLICATING

50. Major entertainment breakthrough of the 1970s, based on laser technology, is RCA's SelectaVision process to convert movies into cartridges for home TV display. This series of sketches shows the important steps in preparation of a SelectaVision hologram cartridge.

ventional approaches for "roll-your-own" home TV, RCA counted on taking a good share of the market from magnetic tapes, conventional movie film systems, etc., by the inexpensive production costs of its novel method. After analyzing engineering and marketing information, the company believed it could provide a compact home TV attachment for under $400, and half hour SelectaVision cartridges for $10 or less.

The SelectaVision programs are not taken directly, but

are converted from movies made on other media. At the processing plant, the original film or video tape is recorded on conventional film by a device known as an electron beam recorder. This film, called the "color encoded master," is processed by light from a helium-neon laser to form a series of holograms on a plastic tape covered with photo resist. Photo resist is a material that becomes increasingly harder when struck by light of greater and greater intensity.

The exposed tape is placed in a chemical solution that eats away the portions of the photo resist not hardened by

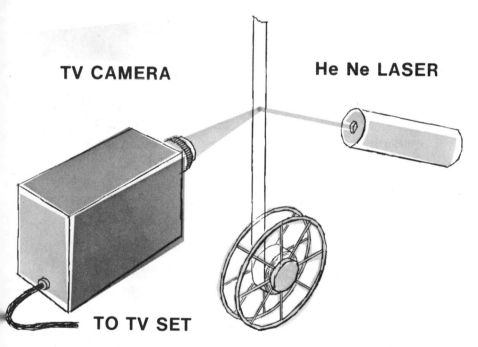

TV CAMERA   **He Ne LASER**

TO TV SET

51. In the SelectaVision player, a small TV camera picks up an image gained by illuminating a vinyl holographic tape with a helium-neon laser. The camera sends signals of this image to play back the tape on the regular TV screen.

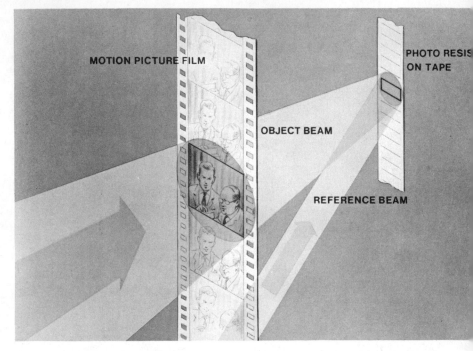

MOTION PICTURE FILM

PHOTO RESIS
ON TAPE

OBJECT BEAM

REFERENCE BEAM

52. This diagram shows how the conventional holographic technique of combining a coherent light reference beam with an object beam is used in the SelectaVision process to convert regular movie film into hologram tape.

the laser beam. The result is "a relief map of photo resist whose hills and valleys, and the spacing between, represent the original color TV program in coded form." The processed tape is referred to as the hologram master.

This master is then plated with a thick coating of nickel metal. When the plastic is stripped off, it leaves a strong piece of flexible metal tape with the holograms impressed on it like a series of engravings. This nickel master can then reproduce the original holograms on vinyl tape when the transparent vinyl is pressed against it by a set of

53. *Small box on top of this color TV set is the SelectaVision cartridge player that allows a set owner to screen his own home TV movies.*

pressure rollers. A single nickel master can be used to turn out thousands of duplicate vinyl tapes.

The vinyl films are then housed in a cartridge for use in the SelectaVision player. The player contains a small TV camera, a helium-neon laser, and reels to pass the vinyl film between camera and laser. When the laser beam shines through the vinyl, the TV camera picks up the images and relays them to the screen of the TV set.

The laser needed for SelectaVision operates on a few watts of power. Its low power requirements make it no hazard to home viewers. In fact, it is far less hazardous than the radiation patterns set up in the normal TV set. Equally important, this laser development is economically competitive with other cartridge TV systems. The plastic tape that holds the hologram material is the same kind of tape used by supermarkets to package meat. As a result, use of the laser provided RCA with a film material costing only about a tenth as much as conventional movie film.

It seemed likely that RCA's experience with an inexpensive laser design could show the way to other home equipment based on coherent light. Thus progress in communications seemed likely to result in a laser in every home by the end of the 1970s.

CHAPTER VI

IT'S ONLY THE BEGINNING

While the laser and such associated technologies as holography are already playing an important role in modern society, it can be said with confidence that laser based systems will have an even greater impact on the world of tomorrow. As more lasers come into use and scientific understanding of the processes involved increases, new uses probably will be discovered that can't even be imagined now.

Even as these pages are written, it's likely that laser applications once predicted to become practical decades in the future may actually be only a few years away because of unexpectedly swift progress in the research laboratory. For example, holography experts have warned for some time that three-dimensional movies present severe technical problems that may not be solved before the 1980s or 1990s. But there are signs today that, as one modern expert has noted, "the future is arriving sooner than it used to."

One significant event is RCA's SelectaVision process detailed in the last chapter. The SelectaVision tape actually consists of a series of holograms rather than conventional two-dimensional film images. The 3-D of the holograms is

54. The streamlined appearance of industrial lasers of the 1970s, such as this high-power, argon-pulsed device, indicated that coherent light systems had come of age.

converted to two dimensions by the TV camera because the goal is to present the pictures on a regular 2-D home TV screen. It does not take a tremendous amount of imagination, though, to foresee development of a different kind of viewing arrangement that would present the holographic information in the film in full three-dimensional glory. At present, the cost of this kind of a viewer would be far too high for home use, but continued development work might well result in a practical production system before the end of this decade.

Meanwhile, the potential use of 3-D displays to simplify many of man's tasks is receiving attention in many quarters. RCA gained a contract from the Navy, based on its SelectaVision work, to study the use of holograms to simplify a reconnaissance pilot's map-storage problems. Aim of the program was development of a holographic display providing the pilot with a full-color, continuously moving three-dimensional display of the territory he was flying over. Not only did this promise a much more readily understandable display, it also did not have the problems of maintaining map-film files or operating the complex optical devices needed for regular film displays.

The possibilities of hologram displays obviously were of interest to all phases of both military and civilian aircraft operation. Being able to look at 3-D displays of runways and the area around airports can play an important part in solving traffic problems of the increasingly con-

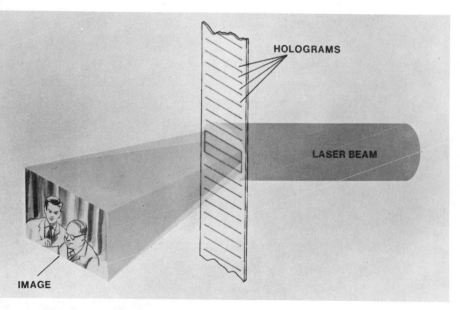

55. Artist's sketch shows how a laser beam is used to project holographic images in RCA's SelectaVision process. A version of this is being studied by RCA for projecting 3-D maps to help guide airplane pilots.

gested airspace. These displays can permit easy landings and take-offs under severe weather conditions where there is close to zero visibility. Eventually, when in-flight holographic picture-taking methods are developed, such a display might finally solve the problem of mid-air collisions.

In the early 1970s, lasers and holograms were under study in many companies and government agencies for air traffic control. This combination suggested replacement of the regular radars used to monitor air flights with a 3-D radar. With this kind of radar, the ground controllers, already complaining of being dangerously overloaded in

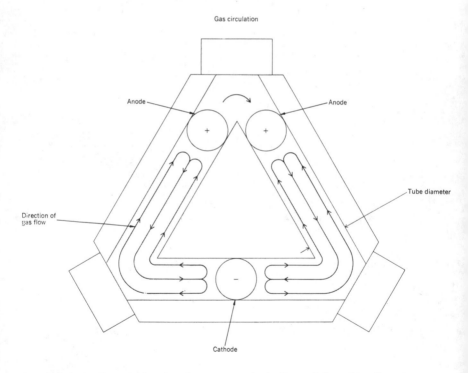

56. Gas flow in a ring laser gyro is indicated by this diagram.

the late 1960s, could easily tell where the various planes under their control were located with moving views of actual planes replacing the hard-to-define blips of today's radar.

The use of lasers also gives promise of easing the navigation problems of all kinds of transport vehicles both in the air and on the ground. The device that is being developed for this application is called a ring laser gyroscope.

The use of light instead of a spinning metal wheel to provide the gyroscope effect was suggested in 1963 by scientists at Sperry Gyroscope Company, Great Neck, New York, the firm whose founder, Elmer Sperry, invented the first gyroscope. They based their reasoning on experiments run in the early 1920s by Michelson. Michelson proved that light could be used to measure the earth's rotation. His experiments consisted of sending a light beam from one hill to another and measuring the time interval required for it to be reflected back.

With the invention of the laser, Sperry scientists noted it was now possible to develop light systems that could provide information on their position in space in relation to the earth's surface. The principle of the original gyroscope is based on the fact that a spinning rotor mounted on special movable frames called gimbals wants to stay where it is in space. Once started rotating, then, the rotor keeps its spin axis always at the same angle with the earth. The gimbal frames, though, move with the vehicle. A series of sensors measures the relative movement of these frames from the rotor position, and this data can be used to determine where the vehicle is at a given time compared to a previously detected position. In the case of an airplane autopilot, a computer can use this information to determine whether the plane's axes are correctly lined up and, if not, to move the controls to restore the craft to the desired alignment.

The fact that a regular gyroscope has many moving parts is one of its drawbacks. Expensive sensors, motors and electronics must be added to start the rotor spinning and to make sure it is always properly located in relation to the gimbals. Michelson's experiments indicated it might be possible to eliminate much of the extra components by monitoring light movement rather than a mechanical device.

By the mid 1960s, work was in progress at Sperry Gyroscope and at many other companies on ring laser gyro designs. At the start of the 1970s, these studies evolved a system based on noble gas lasers. The system, for which an Army development contract was awarded Honeywell Corporation's Systems and Research Division, consisted of two concentric, triangular tubes filled with helium-neon gas. Each of these tubes actually is a gas laser with reflectors placed in all three corners of the triangles. To start the gyro working, all that is needed is to excite the gas mixture to lasing energy levels and cause the gases to flow through the tubes.

The beams are contra-rotating. That is, the beam in one triangle is directed in a clockwise direction and that in the second triangle, counterclockwise. As long as the gyro is stationary, both beams move around the triangle in exactly the same time. When the entire gyro is rotated (at a specified angular rate of inertia multiplied by spin velocity), the light paths appear to change. The gyro movement makes one light path appear to lengthen and

57. *Honeywell Corporation scientist observes tests of glowing ring laser gyroscopes. Each of these gyros provides position data for one of three axes (x, y, and z) that determine a vehicle's position in space.*

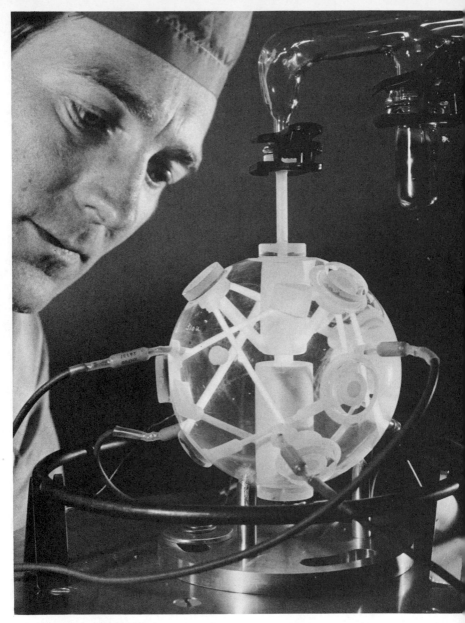

58. Evolution of laser guidance is demonstrated by this picture of a ring laser gyro system developed by Honeywell in the early 1970s for an advanced Army missile. This gyroscope combines the three separate gyros of the previous photograph into a single unit designed

one to shorten. These changes cause variations in the frequency of the two beams. The difference in frequency is measured by sensors and analyzed by a computer to tell what it means in terms of movement of the vehicle. (The importance of the laser to the system is indicated by this frequency comparison. The jumble of frequencies in ordinary light would make it all but impossible to detect any changes caused by variation in the rotation of two beams.)

At the start of the 1970s, much work was still needed to understand all the principles involved in this gyro system and to permit production of a system that would operate dependably for long periods of time. For instance, one thing that tended to limit uses of this gyro to a few minutes' time was the loss of lasing gas through the walls of the glass tubes.

Nonetheless, experimenters were sure this device would eventually be perfected to provide many new applications. Its advantages are impressive: it can be made in very compact form compared to conventional electromechanical gyros, it doesn't need much power to operate, and its simplicity offers the promise of very low cost, so low it can find uses in almost every kind of transport system including the family automobile.

For private aircraft, particularly small light planes, this can be a major breakthrough. Conceivably, the laser gyro could provide the key element in a system costing under $1000 that could allow the personal aircraft pilot to have a foolproof autopilot device for bad weather operation.

---

into a spherical block of quartz. The device at the top is a filling unit that here supplied the tubes with a helium-neon gas mixture that provides the lasing action.

At present, a great many of the light plane accidents result from the pilot's inability to cope with fog, high winds, or severe storms.

Gyro experts forsee laser gyros as playing an important role in highway safety. An inertial system, including the computer, is believed producible for as little as $200 for cars, trucks, or buses. These systems would be tied into the vehicle's power steering system and would monitor the control of the car by the driver. In case of a sudden movement of the vehicle from a normal path—say if a sudden gust of wind hit a vehicle while it was passing another vehicle or if the car hit a slick spot and skidded —the inertial system would almost instantaneously send signals to the controls to remedy the situation.

But the biggest advance in automotive systems the inertial system promises is the realization of hopes for automatic highways. In effect, cars having such a gyro installation have ground-based autopilots for use on specially designed, very accurately surveyed roads. As the car moved onto such a road, an electronic monitor alongside the entrance ramp would send signals to the car's computer outlining the route to be followed. As the car moved along the highway, the gyro would provide the reference from which the computer would control the car's movement. All cars using the highway would also be equipped with sensors that would constantly check the positions of other cars to ensure proper spacing so that no accidents would occur. At roughly fifty-mile intervals, the car would pass electronic devices that would reset the inertial gyro correcting any small errors that might have built up over the previous fifty miles.

Lasers and holograms promise to play important roles

in the predicted home communications centers of the future. These centers, envisioned by such people as one of the founders of RCA, David Sarnoff, would incorporate all kinds of playback equipment, videophones, and devices that would print out the morning or evening newspaper, educational material, notes from business offices, etc. Such a center would link the home directly to all kinds of services from the local school to the supermarket.

The links from the center to the outside world probably would be the laser beam techniques mentioned in the last chapter. In time, the flow of information might be extended outward to other parts of the universe with travelogues of Mars, Jupiter, or Saturn transmitted via laser devices to receiving stations on earth for retransmission to home TV circuits.

Closer to home, hologram processing systems in the home center might be used to provide instant library material. At the start of the 1970s, the potential for storing great amounts of information in small hologram cubes had already been demonstrated. Bell Laboratory scientists, for instance, stored 1000 exposures on one small area of a photographic film by recording each as a uniquely coded hologram. Based on work of this nature, Dr. Brian Thompson, director of the Institute of Optics, Rochester University, New York, pointed to speculation "that a thousand $8\frac{1}{2} \times 11$ pages might be stored in a recording medium only 1 cm^2 in area and 1 cm thick."

For the home communications center of the future, this could be tied in with a laser link to a library. (The library, in turn, could have similar communications arrangements with major libraries in other parts of the country.) Based on some kind of payment system automatically registered on the phone circuits, requests could be made for a book or report. This material, in the form of a master hologram cube, could be placed in an encoder which would send signals through the line to a decoder set containing a second, blank, cube. The cube would then be programmed by the incoming signals to record a duplicate of the original data.

The systems for coding and sending holographic data over long distances are not available at present and might not be for some time to come. However, despite the technical difficulties, it is not beyond the realm of reason that they will be developed. Certainly the transmission of photographs and written material by wire has long been a reality in newspaper work and, more recently, direct transmission of this kind of material by phone became commercially available. The step to sending holograms from one place to another is thus only an extension of existing techniques. In fact, methods of transmitting single holograms will probably precede development of systems for sending 3-D television programs into the home.

A field in which lasers promise to play increasingly important parts in the future is chemistry. Initially, lasers probably will be used to streamline existing methods of making certain kinds of chemicals so that such substances can be made faster and for much lower cost.

D. A. Buddenhagen of Hughes Electronic's Products points out, "Chemical reactions are strongly influenced by the energy levels of the reacting atoms and molecules. Many chemical processes can be speeded up by adding energy. When the internal energy of the system is altered, a reaction takes place, forming new chemical bonds or disrupting others. Some of these reactions are photosensitive and can be influenced by the addition of energy in the form of light."

As improved high-power lasers are developed, coherent light can add completely new compounds to the chemical inventory. Says Buddenhagen, "It is possible to focus the laser beam to extremely high-power densities on the order of ten billion kilowatts per square centimeter. The optical frequency electric field is about one billion volts per centimeter. This is more than the electric field binding the outer electrons (that is, holding them in their orbits around the nucleus) in most atoms and molecules. Thus the laser may be used to form highly reactive ions and, under certain conditions, to initiate the formation of new chemicals."

Apart from affecting chemical reactions, lasers from the start were vital new tools for researchers in this field. The laser beam can be used to detect the presence of different elements in a chemical substance and thus has been universally adopted by chemical research laboratories as a dependable instrument for chemical analysis.

The laser has already found a number of applications in medicine, as mentioned earlier, and undoubtedly will find more. In addition to its use in surgery, lasers and the various forms of holography, including acoustic systems, will most likely form the basis for analytical instruments to study the condition of man's internal organs. Combined with X rays, ultrasonics, and other systems for doing this, laser systems can speed the trend toward preventive medicine. In this approach, physicians will use their new sources of information to detect dangerous changes in the body and remedy them before these can result in damaging illness. Holographic pictures or movies, taken at regular intervals, for example, might feed data into a computer that would promptly warn of unusual variations in body processes.

The potential of lasers and holography in medicine was amply demonstrated by the intense interest of experts briefed on the technique at the Seventh National Biomedical Sciences Instrumentation meeting at the University of Michigan in May 1969. Research scientists from Conductron Corporation described how real image holograms are made and presented a series of 3-D pictures made of clay models of a human brain, section of stomach wall, parts of the intestine, etc. Though told it might be some time before ways could be developed to take such pictures inside the human body without surgery, most people were impressed just with the immediate possibility of using such 3-D pictures as illustrations in medical or biological textbooks.

In fact, once costs are reduced, laser-produced 3-D pictures promise to greatly simplify the entire educational process. The nature of three-dimensional holograms is such that several times more information can be provided in each picture compared to two-dimensional illustrations. In addition, whether the reader is studying about automobile engines or complex mathematical surfaces, he will find it much easier to visualize the subject if he can see it in three-dimensional form.

A little over a year after the University of Michigan meeting, doctors were being shown experimental holograms of human tissue taken of sections inside the human body. This work, based on acoustic holography, was revealed to the medical profession at the December 1970 meeting of the Radiological Society of North America in

Chicago by Dr. Melvin Sikov of Battelle-Northwest Laboratories. Demonstrating live TV images of tissue, Sikov stated, "Using this device, it is possible to look at any single focal plane as you search—with sound—through the body cavity." The method provided pictures of some internal parts of the body that previously could not be obtained at all. Among the many breakthroughs this promised, noted Sikov, was a way to locate exactly blood clots for surgical removal.

The field of dentistry also is closely studying possible laser applications. In late 1970, for instance, results of clinical studies of the use of laser welding to assemble bridgework were disclosed by experimenters from Orange Memorial Hospital and International Laser Systems, both of Orlando, Florida. Their studies indicated assembling dentures with a neodymium-doped gas laser had a number of advantages over the conventional process of doing the work by heating gold solder with a blowtorch.

The laser produced much stronger bonds, equal in strength to the base material, and, by eliminating distortion due to uneven cooling, shrinkage, etc., insured that accurate bridgework could be made even by relatively unskilled workers. The laser method cut assembly time for a typical denture from over an hour to a few minutes. Most important, the speed and simplicity of the operation made it possible to try out a partially finished denture in the patient's mouth, then take it to a nearby laboratory, and have it back, ready for installation, a short time afterward. Today, a patient may have to go days or weeks with empty space in his mouth before his new false teeth are completed.

A happier turn of events than needing dentures results

59. & 60. *Laser technology promises to make it possible for doctors to make new breakthroughs in analyzing and curing human ailments. An example is the ultrasonic holography system shown in*

from improved dental care that prevents loss of
Here, too, the laser is being examined for help in
vancing health. Laser drills, now in use on an experimen.
tal basis, appear likely to aid dentists in making much
more painless repairs to teeth with much more accurate
control of the surface being drilled. The use of lasers to
"glaze" teeth someday may keep the occurrence of cavi-
ties to a minimum. In this approach, the laser beam is
used to apply special protective coating around healthy
teeth so that decay germs cannot attack the natural
tooth material.

Lasers eventually will dramatically widen the bounda-

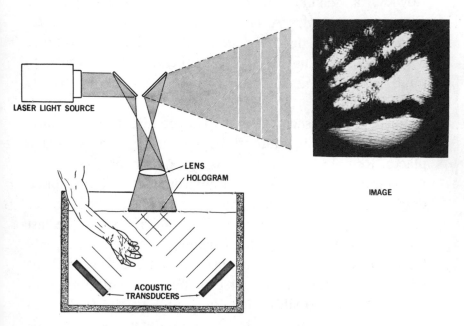

*these pictures. The diagram shows how two sound beams are used
to create a hologram of a part of a body on the surface of a liquid.
The system can be adjusted to provide images of almost any kind
of body material.*

ɾ all types of photography. Holography, of course, is ᴛriking example, but lasers will do much for conven-ᴛonal photography as well. Laser illumination, for instance, is a powerful substitute for conventional floodlights and flashlamps. By the late 1960s, a number of companies had developed camera systems using laser light that could take pictures in the dark. The laser beam ulluminated the subject, but unless an observer looked directly into the beam, which even then only would seem to be a dot of light, the illumination would, in effect, be invisible.

Some companies studied systems making the laser device into both illumination source and camera. Robert S. Rowley, a scientist at Perkin-Elmer Corporation, told *Electronic Design,* "A laser TV camera would have essentially infinite depth of field. Objects at any distance would be in focus. The first application that comes to mind is remote newscasting without your having to lug studio lights."

Variations of such systems also promise compact cameras for mapping and surveying many hard-to-reach places. Remote laser picture-taking equipment could monitor important changes in the environment of uninhabited deserts or the polar caps. Such systems may be used to survey the ocean bottom, a place considered to be the last great storehouse of important materials for man, but only three to four per cent mapped to date. Laser cameras might also bring us the first pictures of still unknown deep sea life—possibly including proof of the fabled sea serpents of Scotland's lochs. These systems could also be the prototype for more powerful cameras that may, in the future, be landed on other planets of the solar system to provide spectacular views of these strange environments.

IT'S ONLY THE BEGINNING

In future decades, though, the most crucial contr. of the laser may come, as Dr. Sidney Benson predicte all-chemical devices. For this kind of laser may resol the energy crisis already threatening to bring the wheels of today's civilization to a grinding halt.

Man has come to realize that the fuels he depends on to keep the increasingly complicated operations of modern society going can run out. Despite the findings of new supplies of oil and gas under the oceans and on the frigid slopes of the Arctic regions, the increased needs of expanding world population are more than keeping up with capacity. This was demonstrated in the United States in 1970 when some parts of the eastern seaboard were threatened with rationing of these fuels because of short supplies of the oil and gas companies.

Electric power is also affected by fuel shortages, because many generating plants use gas, coal, or oil to generate steam or to run gas turbines that generate part of the electric output. Shortages of electric power were apparent in large cities as the 1960s came to a close. New York City, for instance, on quite a few hot summer days suffered "brownouts" because demands of electric air conditioners exceeded the electricity available from the power companies.

With increasing population and more and more electric devices coming into use, matters promised to become even worse in the last decades of the twentieth century. Electric company officials knew more power plants were needed. However, some people complained of the pollution from fuels used in steam-operated electric plants and, apart from this, the availability of running water for new hydroelectric plants was limited. For this reason, in the 1950s

'60s, the attention of power experts turned to nu-
technology. Harnessing the energy in the atom prom-
ed enormous amounts of power from small amounts of
material.

Thus during the 1960s, the first atomic power plants based on fission were built and placed in operation. Plans were drawn up to build hundreds more atomic fission plants in later years. However, at this point, some scientists began to oppose such plants as dangerous health hazards. (In a fission plant, heat released when atoms are split is used to heat a working fluid that then rotates a turbine to generate electricity.) Despite the most stringent safe-guards, they said, when atoms were split, some radiation escaped into the environment.

In a survey conducted by University of California sci-entists Professor John Gofman and Dr. Arthur Tamplin, it was concluded that the government standard for maxi-mum dosage from peaceful nuclear applications was too high. These researchers estimated 32,000 people a year might die from radiation-induced illness unless the dosage rate was reduced to 1/100th of the government standard. In late 1970, Nobel Laureate Dr. Linus Pauling went even further. He stated that if every American received the high energy radiation dosage allowed for peacetime use of atomic energy, as many as 96,000 persons a year would die from leukemia and other forms of cancer. He advocated a ban on atomic power plants.

Thus there were two very undesirable alternatives fac-ing the United States at the start of the 1970s. Nuclear power based on fission could be banned completely, but this could result in severe power shortages and perhaps economic depression in the future. Or fission plants could be built in sufficient numbers to meet future need, with increased health dangers to mankind.

The answer, some experts said, was to develop the power of the atom in a different way—through fusing atoms together instead of splitting them. The fusion process also would give off heat—in fact, several times the heat of an equivalent amount of fission material. But fusion, since it pushes things together rather than shatters them, inherently does not send stray particles of radiation into the surrounding region.

This made sense, except for one thing: it requires tremendous levels of temperature and pressure to fuse atoms together and, despite many years of research, all the problems had yet to be solved as the 1960s ended.

Dr. Francis Chen of the UCLA School of Engineering and Applied Science, a pioneer in fusion research, points out that these processes call for fusing atomic nuclei by heating them "up to 100 million degrees centigrade, or temperatures higher than those found at the center of the sun. At such temperatures, the outer electrons of the nuclei are stripped off, leaving a hot gaseous stream of free electrons and free nuclei known as plasma." It is this flowing plasma that provides the heat energy needed for power generation.

One problem was to get the tremendous temperatures needed to create the plasma. This could be done on a laboratory scale at the start of the 1970s. A second need was to contain the plasma. Obviously, Chen notes, any conventional container will melt in fractions of a second. Here scientists came up with the idea of a magnetic bottle. Such a bottle is not a solid material, but an extremely powerful magnetic field developed by special magnets that on the charged electrons in the plasma to keep them in carefully controlled area.

However, nuclear scientists at the start of the 1970s had not been able to build a "leakproof" magnetic bottle. After relatively short times, parts of the plasma would build up to greater densities than in the general plasma mass and break down the magnetic bottle.

As this is written, though, Dr. Chen is working with lasers in a program he believes may overcome the difficulty. Infrared lasers, he notes, can be used to give information on plasma properties. And, if infrared lasers more powerful than those available in 1970 could be perfected, his calculations indicated they could solve a dual purpose in magnetic containment. The warning sign of leakage, he points out, is a small bump developing on the dense plasma mass, and the counteraction is to force the bump back into the main mass.

A powerful infrared laser, Chen theorized, could do the job, pushing hard enough to force the bump back, but light enough to keep the bump from coming out on the other side of the contained plasma.

Even with such a device, there still remained the problem of continuously developing the fantastic amounts of energy required to raise temperatures to the fusion plasma levels. The invention of the all-chemical laser in 1969, though, finally offered a possible tool for this.

Because the all-chemical laser does not require optical pumping of electrical energy, it theoretically can achieve a conversion efficiency of close to 100 per cent. Nor does it have the power limitations of other lasers. In principle, Dr. Benson stresses, the power output would be limited only by the size of the optical chamber and the rate at which chemicals could be fed into the chamber.

"This development," says Benson, "is capable of ushering in a new era in atomic energy, an era in which mankind will have at his disposal incredible amounts of energy. In time, all-chemical lasers seem likely to serve as the method of initiating controlled atomic fusion, opening the door for such things as electrical power plants which use sea water instead of uranium. With atomic fusion, one pound of sea water could produce the energy currently obtained from one million pounds of coal."

Dr. Chen summed it up, "To some people, it may seem odd that so many scientists are devoting years and even decades of their lives to a project whose ultimate success is not at all certain, or at least many light years away. But the potential benefits of controlled nuclear fusion to mankind in terms of unlimited, safe, pollution-free energy production are so enormous, they're worth any effort."

INDEX